WILDERNESS

IN A

CHANGING WORLD

CONTRIBUTORS

Clinton P. Anderson

James Bonner

Paul Brooks

David Brower

Albert E. Burke

James K. Carr

John A. Carver, Jr.

Edward P. Cliff

John B. Condliffe

Edward C. Crafts

Lincoln H. Day

William C. Gibson

Harold Gilliam

James P. Gilligan

Arie J. Haagen-Smit

George Hartzog, Jr.

Clark Kerr

Chauncey D. Leake

Luna B. Leopold

Albert Lepawsky

Ashley Montagu

Sigurd F. Olson

Margaret W. Owings

T. Eric Reynolds

Paul B. Sears

William E. Siri

Charles H. Stoddard

Edgar Wayburn

Peggy Wayburn

WILDERNESS
in a Changing World

Edited by BRUCE M. KILGORE

with a foreword by PEGGY WAYBURN

SIERRA CLUB ✦ SAN FRANCISCO

THE SIERRA CLUB is a national conservation organization founded in 1892 by John Muir to explore, enjoy, and protect the nation's scenic resources of parks, wilderness, wildlife, and the recreation derived from them. There are more than 37,000 members; 27,000 have joined the club in the last decade in support of an active program to preserve the scenic resources. The main headquarters and several chapters are in California. There are also chapters in Nevada, the Northwest, Midwest, and Southwest, the Rockies, the Atlantic Coast, and Texas. The program is in independent support of the public interest as the club sees it. The club is managed by an elected board of directors and is affiliated with the Natural Resources Council of America and the International Union for Conservation.

The club has been well aware of the dual aspect of conservation, calling on the one hand for much wise utilization of resources on at least ninety per cent of our land, and on the other hand for some wise preservation on at most ten per cent of our land. The first kind of conservation is difficult enough, the second ever so much more so. In the effort to further both, the club had roles in creating the Forest Service and the National Park Service. It has profound respect for the people and achievements of both agencies but reserves the right occasionally to disagree with them.

Membership is open to those who are sympathetic with the club's purposes and wish to support its program. Dues are nominal.

Address: Mills Tower, San Francisco; 25 West 45th Street, New York; 710 Dupont Circle Building, Washington, D.C.

FOREWORD

In a time when we seem increasingly bent on cutting our ties with the earth, it is not easy to put wilderness into clear perspective, nor to measure what it means to us. For wilderness, in the final analysis, is the earth itself and its flora and fauna as God made it—or, if you will, as man first found it. It has supported human life from the beginning and supplied the raw material for our civilization. It has challenged the spirit and mind of man since he started to think, and much of his thinking has been devoted to finding more efficient ways of conquering and utilizing it. In a very basic sense, we belong to wilderness, even though we decided long ago that it belongs to us.

Perhaps no other country has been more profoundly linked to wilderness than ours. The rigors of wilderness living toughened the first American settlers, shaped their mores, and forged their spirits. The fittest survived to write a memorable history. We wrote it in wood and smoke and wasted watersheds, in grain and dust, in gold and leached-out tailings and muddied waters. And with our ingenuity and know-how, we achieved in a brief two centuries what took a millennium in other parts of the world: we consumed almost totally what was once considered a limitless wilderness, one of the richest, most varied, and magnificent of all.

But if the word *conservation* came late into our vocabulary—and its honest, intelligent practice came even later—still it did come. Today it is accepted, even acclaimed. Beauty has become a political issue. We have stopped short of wringing the last penny out of our wilderness and have established a wilderness system, protected by law.

For these giant strides, credit is due in many places. Starting with George Marsh and John Muir, it is due the dedicated conservationists who saw the truth and weren't afraid to speak it. It is due the people who loved the land enough to let it alone. It is even due the developers who by their blatant and continued destruction of the landscape opened so many eyes to the need for change. And it is due, at least in some part, to the unique forum known as the Wilderness Conference.

The initial contribution of the Wilderness Conference was, of course, the fact that it recognized wilderness as a resource worth convening over. The timing of the first conference was right, too—it is doubtful that it could have been established sooner than 1949.

The first Wilderness Conference set a pattern that has persisted ever since: the bringing together of the wilderness user and the wilderness administrator to discuss common problems. However, the subject matter of that conference—specific problems in the Sierra Nevada—proved to be simply a beginning. Since then, ideas have soared, and the scope and content of each conference have grown enormously. In the eight following conferences, many aspects of wilderness have been explored.

The problems of managing wild lands have been probed, as have the difficulties of establishing and protecting wilderness. Wilderness has been considered from the scientific viewpoint, as a laboratory—ever more valuable as a control for measurement of our environment. The inspirational value of wilderness has been weighed —its pleasures and its influence on the health of people. Wilderness as a part of the cultural pattern of America, what lies ahead for wilderness, its vulnerability, how it can survive the increasing demands of a burgeoning population—the topics have ranged widely.

It is noteworthy that the Wilderness Conference traditionally packs a tremendous volume and variety of ideas into a two-day session. Yet two years later there is always more to be talked about, more fresh material to be explored. Wilderness itself does not grow, of course, but our evaluation of it and our attitudes do. It is a unique function of the conference to focus on and to clarify our changing concepts of the wilderness resource.

A man's feelings and ideas about wilderness tend to be as personal as his religion. The men and women who have addressed the Wilderness Conferences during the years have expressed a wide spectrum of personal viewpoints. Albert Burke said at the Ninth Conference that the meetings attract "great men with great ideas." Some of these men have been identified with wilderness and the conservation movement—men like the late beloved Olaus Murie and Howard Zahniser. Others have been well-known outdoorsmen and authors, such as William O. Douglas and Sigurd Olson. But an extraordinary variety of talented people—artists, scientists, physicians, bureaucrats, scholars, demographers, members of the clergy, members of the Congress, and others—have taken part, too. Many of them not connected directly

Redwood Creek and the tallest known redwoods

David Swanlund

OUR LAST CHANCE

For a Redwood National Park

This is the last of an ancient race, in a land of majestic forms . . .
This is the land of the last Redwoods

Redwoods, vine maples, and ferns along Lost Man Creek

In a too-crowded, too-synthetic new world,
man still has some simple, ancient needs:
a hunger for solitude, a thirst for beauty, a craving for wildness.

This is not a land that belongs to us.
   We cannot destroy it without destroying something in us.

Redwood Creek in the proposed national park

REDWOOD CREEK is the place—the last chance for a real Redwood National Park. Trees that were saplings on the first Christmas still live here. The tallest known trees were discovered on Redwood Creek recently by the National Geographic Society.

The park would include large blocks of unbroken forest, bottom stands of record height, sunny, spacious flats for campgrounds, superior slope redwoods, and a wild sweep of ocean beach with herds of Roosevelt elk. Yet the largest park envisioned by preservationists would still leave more than 94 percent of the redwood forest land in California available for commercial timber production.

Life's urge to survive is the force
that shaped the redwoods and their world of wildness,
that made them one of the great miracles . . . .

Bull Creek Flat, Humboldt Redwoods State Park

Philip Hyde

Man, if he is too impatient to care,
can end this miracle, can terminate a chain of life
going back without interruption to an old eternity . . .

Bald Hills Ridge forest, partly logged

Industry's "sensible plan" would open 260,000 acres of cut-over lands to recreation. This may be good enough for those who prefer their red-woods lying down, converted to fences, panels and siding, piling, posts, pulp, and picnic tables. But is it good enough for you?

The richest nation on earth as yet preserves none of its finest coast redwoods in a Federal park or monument, except for a tiny tract in Muir Woods National Monument.

*July 24, 1964: Modern tractor logging by Arcata Redwood
Company in the heart of the proposed Redwood National Park.*

October 24, 1964: The same slope three months later (note circled stump).

Logging near
Little Lost Man Creek

Logging continues at a rapid rate in the Prairie Creek Watershed (photos at left), one mile from Gold Bluffs Seashore and one mile from Prairie Creek Redwoods State Park. Preservation of an adequate sample of redwoods in a Redwood National Park can provide an end to such logging by Arcata Redwood Company throughout the area south of Prairie Creek State Park and along Redwood Creek.

Some may be willing to settle for a false-front redwood national park—a thin line of trees shielding the highway traveler from the destruction beyond. Or for an existing state park relabeled a national park. Such bargain-basement national parks may cost little, but they save little too. Generations of Americans will gain if we keep our last virgin redwoods vertical, not prone.

Avenue of the Giants   *Philip Hyde*

Wildness made man but he cannot make it.
He can only spare it.

(Text adapted in part from *The Last Redwoods*.)

with wilderness have discovered their own deep, latent interest in it by participating in the conferences. All have found wilderness worth considering.

The important ideas they have brought to the Wilderness Conferences have been recorded in the proceedings of the conferences. These books—totaling five with this volume—form a notable addition to wilderness literature. Nowhere is there a more succinct or comprehensive exploration of the subject.

Not only ideas, but significant conservation action has sprung from the Wilderness Conferences, too. It was at an early conference that Howard Zahniser launched his first proposal for a Wilderness Bill. From a later session, a suggestion of David Brower was taken to spark the formation of the Outdoor Recreation Resources Review Commission. The conferences are recognized more and more as major forums for the exchange and development of conservation ideas, many of which may affect the public use of wilderness. A number of administrative policies and decisions affecting wilderness have been officially announced at Wilderness Conferences; many others have undoubtedly been influenced and shaped.

Successive sessions of the Wilderness Conference have attracted ever larger attendance: over 1,200 people registered for the ninth. But what a conference sets in motion does not stop with the people who sit through it. They may carry the message many times further themselves, even as the books will do. Important action may ensue. Increasingly good and wide coverage by the press, radio, and TV will reach untold thousands more. And these media reach the people who, in the long run, are the most important to the survival of wilderness—the men in the street, the citizenry, the voters. This is really the conference's most vital function of all—to reach many people and awaken in them an understanding of wilderness.

Olaus Murie said in his beautiful, simple way at one of the first Berkeley meetings: "You must come to understand wilderness, then you come to love it." And that is the most important thing of all.

PEGGY WAYBURN

CONTENTS

INTRODUCTION

The Wilderness Conferences began modestly in 1949 when a handful of people met in Berkeley. The first few conferences were relatively small and confined themselves to the Sierra Nevada, but the time quickly arrived when the size of the conference grew beyond the bounds of Berkeley and the Sierra Nevada.

Under the guidance of Sierra Club Director Charlotte Mauk and of Doris (Mrs. Richard M.) Leonard, the scope of the conferences broadened and they began to move across the country in interest and in a search for outstanding speakers in a great many fields related to wilderness.

During the 1951 Conference, the late Howard Zahniser of The Wilderness Society first proposed the idea of the Wilderness Bill, and only last year, some 13 years later, it was enacted and signed into law.

The subsequent Wilderness Conferences have been highly successful. They have served the country, wilderness, and the Sierra Club in a fashion that could not have been anticipated in 1949. The Biennial Wilderness Conferences have become one of the principal educational activities of the Sierra Club. They draw together noted experts from across the United States and around the world.

These conferences, while they are sponsored by the Sierra Club and in part supported by the Sierra Club, are also supported by many other people, by grants, gifts, and contributions of all kinds. They have become so important in the conservation movement as it relates to wilderness that there seems little likelihood that they will be abandoned for many, many years to come.

The Ninth Wilderness Conference is the proper occasion to pay tribute to two events that have occurred since the last conference was held. The first of these is a birth, and the other is a death, and they are both related. The birth was the National Wilderness System embodied in the "Wilderness Bill" legislation enacted by Congress and signed into law last year by the President. The death was that of Howard Zahniser on May 5, 1964.

[21

Believing that some means of long-time wilderness preservation must be found, Dr. Zahniser said in the midst of the now famous controversy, "We must recognize that all our land is destined to be put to some human use. If any of it is to be preserved in its natural condition, it must be as the result of a deliberate setting aside of it *for our human use of it* in a natural condition."

It was in March of 1951 at the Second Wilderness Conference that Howard Zahniser had first spelled out in detail a proposal for the establishment of the National Wilderness Preservation System. The first of the Wilderness Bills was introduced into Congress five years later. Eight more years were to elapse, however, before it would become law.

Howard Zahniser, who conceived the Wilderness Preservation System, and did more than any other man alive to champion its creation, died just three months too soon to see the final act signed by the President. With the passing of Howard Zahniser, we lost one of the truly great conservationists of the first half of this century.

On behalf of the Sierra Club and conservationists everywhere, I wish to dedicate this volume of the Biennial Wilderness Conference proceedings to the memory of Howard Zahniser. We hope the conferences themselves will serve as a memorial to him and to his dedication to the living wilderness.

WILLIAM E. SIRI
President, Sierra Club

I

WILDERNESS IN CRISIS

Keynote Address: Wilderness and Man in 2065
WILLIAM E. SIRI

The Pressure of People
LINCOLN H. DAY

Comprehensive Planning and the Dragon to Slay
LUNA B. LEOPOLD

The Economic Aspects of Conservation
JOHN B. CONDLIFFE
with
DAVID BROWER

JAMES P. GILLIGAN, *Chairman*

KEYNOTE ADDRESS:
WILDERNESS AND MAN IN 2065

≫ *William E. Siri*

Wilderness and conservation have at times seemed unfortunate choices of words. They seemed to many people busily engaged in an expanding and prosperous country to call up vague images of passionate eccentrics who were bent on stopping the world, halting progress, and demanding we all go native. The words themselves, however, had little to do with the images. The images they evoked depended on the prevailing attitude toward what the conservationist advocated. In a world where productive use of any and all land was regarded a moral obligation, and where society believed in the inalienable right of an owner to do whatever he pleased with the land, the image of the conservationist was not always flattering.

Times and attitudes have changed. One hundred ninety million Americans with more time on their hands are beginning to look more critically at the world about them. They are beginning to ask why the world must look like a junk yard. They are demanding more open space and parks and more opportunities for outdoor recreation and for solitude in natural surroundings. They are wondering why they do not have access to more beaches, rivers, lakes, forests and meadows, and they are resenting the dense herding in the places they can reach. In short, scores of millions, without realizing it, are fast becoming de facto conservationists.

Tens of millions have also discovered wilderness. For those to whom it is a new experience, wilderness may be a vision of majestic scenery, of trees, rocks, streams, and mountains, collectively called a national park or national forest. Even from the road, the campsites, or the peripheral trail, it offers novelty, contrast, and a hint of adventure. If it seems at first a strange and unforgiving environment, there is always the handsome, immaculately uniformed ranger whose courteous and confident bearing gives reassurance.

To the wilderness sophisticate, wilderness is a necessary piece of his life. It is not only a place; it is an addiction. It offers adventure and excitement, but it also offers tranquility and solace that equal or transcend that of the cathedral.

There is a small group of people, among whom I count myself, to whom true wilderness is all but non-existent on this continent. This is wilderness without trails and far removed from all evidence of man's works. Parts of the Coast Ranges of Canada and Alaska and the Polar Plateau are such places.

Congress defines wilderness in this fashion:

A wilderness, in contrast with those areas where man and his own works dominate the landscape, is hereby recognized as an area where the earth and its community of life are untrammeled by man, where man himself is a visitor who does not remain. An area of wilderness is further defined to mean in this Act an area of undeveloped Federal land retaining its primeval character and influence, without permanent improvements or human habitation, which is protected and managed so as to preserve its natural conditions and which (1) generally appears to have been affected primarily by the forces of nature, with the imprint of man's work substantially unnoticeable; (2) has outstanding opportunities for solitude or a primitive and unconfined type of recreation; (3) has at least five thousand acres of land and is of sufficient size as to make practicable its preservation and use in an unimpaired condition; and (4) may also contain ecological, geological, or other features of scientific, educational, scenic, or historical value.

No matter how one defines wilderness or subjectively views it, a common desire and need for wilderness are with us now. None but the politically blind, the intellectually halt, and the morally lame could fail to respond to the growing demand for wilderness that an emergent awareness of it has created. It does not require great depth of perception to see this in the formalized segment of the conservation movement. It is obvious in the rapid proliferation of organized groups across the country dedicated to preserving some piece of the natural scene. They include innumerable neighborhood committees that spring to life spontaneously to halt a probing freeway or stay the execution of a condemned tree on a city street. They range upward to the national organizations bent on preserving great tracts of forests and mountains, beaches, wild rivers, and unique scenic wonders.

The growth is even more evident in the membership of these organizations. The Sierra Club grows almost ten times as fast as the population of the country.

These signs and symptoms should dispel any illusion that the conservation movement is peopled solely by long-haired nature lovers, posy pluckers, little old ladies in tennis shoes, and other eccentrics and their well-meaning dupes. They should also dispel any doubts that conservation, in all its forms and directions, will shortly become a major political force in the country.

Here in mid-twentieth century, millions of us with ordinary instincts and perception have finally been shocked into the realization that what the visionary giants of the past predicted has almost come to pass. Malthus may not have had wilderness specifically in mind, but the threat to wilderness of limitless expansion in numbers of people was implicit in his contentions. Only now are the voices of Thoreau, Muir, and others becoming meaningful to everyone. With the freedom that an advancing technology gives us, we are able now to look about us and see only more people, their numbers expanding almost visibly before us; more buildings to house and amuse them; more roads to transport them; and more garbage, pollutants, and sewage created by them. With frightening speed our remaining open space and natural scenery are occupied, built on, paved over, inundated, consumed, and otherwise forced into productive use.

Does this seem a grim picture of man's wanton destruction of his own living quarters? Not at all. It is a familiar picture of man following his instincts, or on closer inspection, an equally familiar diagram of his normal fumbling course toward the solution of problems. A modest endowment of reason enables us to tinker with our living quarters, but the endowment is not large enough to anticipate and circumvent the dangers in doing so until they threaten our welfare. That stage has arrived for wilderness.

At this point let me engage you in a bit of fantasy that is the product of fictional hindsight. Some of this vision may excite and reassure you; part of it you may find offensive. If it is the latter, don't quarrel with me. Vent your rage on the crystal ball that revealed the Wilderness Conference Keynote Address of 2065.

*　*　*　*　*

Twenty-five years have elapsed since the last Wilderness Conference. There has been no need for one in the intervening years. Even now it is held only to monitor the adequacy and stability of primitive lands and natural scenic and recreational resources called for in the constitutional amendment providing for the master plan on land and water use. We have come far in reconciling ancient conflicts on land

and water use. Many related problems that plagued mankind a hundred years ago have been solved.

Well into the present century the steady expansion in the human population, though diminishing in rate, continued as a serious threat to mankind. For more than a decade past, however, our population has stabilized at 310 million. Moreover, stability is now assured by our profound knowledge of ourselves and our society, by the technical means at our disposal, and, of course, by law. As we all know from its troubled history, the population problem was not solved quickly or easily. Widespread efforts to cope with the population growth did not get underway until the middle of the last century. To achieve control required more understanding of biological mechanisms and social forces than was then available. This came with the flourishing of these sciences later in the century. Complete control finally came with changing attitudes that accompanied intensification of the population problem. Some of the mores persisting well through the last century now seem quaint, or would, were it not for their almost tragic consequences.

Society in most civilized parts of the world now accepts two children as optimum, and three as a large family. Three is the number at which we begin to engender in ourselves a sense of guilt and impropriety. Contrast this with what our sociologists tell us was the prevailing attitude a century ago. Parents with five and six children viewed their brood with satisfaction and contentment and faced their neighbors with pride—a pride based on tradition, a long-held belief in the sanctity of procreation, and a confused sense of achievement. A woman with a dozen children was publicly acclaimed a hero, treated with affectionate reverence, and in the word of the day was "blessed." Today this unfortunate mother would face condemnation by society for her excessive proliferation. But, as we also know, this would be almost impossible because long before an aberrant mother had reached this tragic state, simple and effective measures prescribed by law would have spared her onerous burden and humiliation.

A hundred years ago man began to emerge from a century-long transition period that followed in the wake of the industrial revolution. It was a period of final exploration of every last niche on his globe, and he proclaimed all of it his living space. He had taken inventory of all his riches, his resources and his real estate, and in characteristic fashion promptly committed every bit of both for whatever the market offered. More important, it was a period of experiment in his attitudes, his institutions, and his way of living. And it was, in its later stages, a period of technological and scientific growth that surpassed at times his capacity to adjust to it.

Looking back with the sureness of hindsight [even if fictional], a clear picture of man and his machines emerges. We can understand why, a century ago, the rapid advances in technology and science evoked fear, apprehension, and even open hostility among conservationists of the day. Technical ingenuity seemed to be serving man's ultimate ruin and the ruin of spiritual and esthetic values of everything else as well.

It is characteristic of man no less than of animals to be suspicious and fearful of any new situation into which he is thrust too rapidly. In this sense, the future offers the least security. It is novel and obscure and unavoidable. There are no clear landmarks for guidance and few cues for comprehension. It was no wonder that people were sometimes apprehensive of seemingly fantastic new machines and new sources of immense energy. They had just learned to release nuclear energy and were torn between fascination and terror.

What some men failed to realize a century ago was that new sources of energy and machines, along with better insight into themselves and the world about them, were in the end their salvation. They alone made it possible to enjoy the best of two worlds: one natural, to be enjoyed in its primitive state; the other mechanized, comfortable, and productive without effort. Only our advanced technology and sources of vast energy released us from the tedious labor that would otherwise be needed to survive and gave us the time and the means to pursue a creative life with a freedom and variety that were inconceivable a century ago. Such technology and energy also enabled 300 million people to live uncramped in a country formerly thought overcrowded with 200 million.

Most important in the context of today's discussion, energy and machines enabled man to restore vast regions of the country to their natural state and preserve them for his own enjoyment.

We have come to realize that energy and machines do not in themselves destroy the natural and esthetic qualities of the land. In effect, they permit its preservation and restoration. In contrast we have seen in primitive countries every last vestige of forest and natural beauty ruthlessly destroyed by man with his bare hands in his struggle to survive. Without energy and machines, 300 million people could not survive in the confines of the United States. In the struggle to do so, they would consume the forests, replow and overgraze the lands, and foul the waters and atmosphere. What we have achieved with our technology is clear: personal freedom, a world that is beautiful and secure, and public lands for recreation and wilderness enjoyment that far exceed the most hopeful aspirations of the mid-twentieth century.

Today great bands of natural lands and forests stretch across the country from coast to coast and from Mexico northward beyond the arctic circle. Large expanses of prairie, desert, and the hardwood forest of the midwest and east are restoring themselves. The ancient trees of the old Redwood National Park in Northern California are being joined by vigorous young trees spreading southward along the coast. The vast buffer zones of managed lands paralleling the wilderness bands provide the immediate daily recreational needs of the millions who live in the adjacent urban strips.

Decades ago our rivers and streams ceased to be fouled by the wastes of civilization. Our atmosphere has never been freer of contaminants since man first learned to use fire.

A hundred years ago some 800 species of animals faced extinction. Seventy-five succumbed, among them, the Indian rhinoceros, the Yeti, and the hydroelectric engineer.

The Bureau of Reclamation has for several decades conscientiously discharged its responsibility for restoring the land. The Bureau is now busily engaged in removing many of the long useless dams and other works that were once marvels of engineering achievement. Hoover Dam and a few others are preserved as historical monuments. But Glen Canyon Dam has been dismantled, as have other dams in the Colorado River.

Rampart Dam on the Yukon River in Alaska remains as a monument to folly. It was, as we all know, rendered useless shortly before completion by far more economical power from modern sources. The gates were never closed to form the reservoir. But Rampart served a purpose. It was one of the costly mistakes that accelerated the evolution of modern concepts of land and water use.

*   *   *   *   *

But today is not 2065; it is still 1965. This is a day near the end of the period of transition we imagined in which the compulsion for economic, political, and population growth have had, and still have, the force of sacred dogma. We are still confronted with strong remnants of ancient beliefs that productive use of land and water is the only justifiable use. We continue remorselessly to expand in numbers. Our rivers, streams, and atmosphere are still fouled by the excrescences of civilization. A Redwood National Park has not yet been established, let alone become venerable; Rampart Dam has not yet been built to be abandoned for want of a useful purpose. The entire country is bound together with highways and transmission lines like a gigantic package wrapped and tied by an idiot. And the whole of it is festooned with gaudy signs screaming for our attention wherever we turn.

Signs of change, however, are about us. Wilderness areas, shores, rivers, and threatened species are being preserved. Science and engineering are advancing steadily against pollution from the wastes and by-products of civilization. We have as a nation recognized the danger of uncontrolled population growth. A major change in ancient attitudes on birth control is imminent, and primitive but effective means for exercising this control are at hand. New sources of immense energy are also at hand, and still greater energy in yet smaller packages will come soon to give us greater freedom of time and means to enjoy the lands and waters that energy also frees from labor.

Perhaps most important, conservation of our scenic resources and the concept of an esthetically pleasing world are now a part of national policy. Major pieces of legislation have already been enacted. Legislators have sensed the pressure of the conservation movement and the politically astute are responding.

Regretfully, the Bureau of Reclamation and the Corps of Engineers are still building hydroelectric dams in some of our most priceless real estate instead of dismantling them. But let us have faith. Surely the next generation of engineers will discover that not all things need the helping hand of technical ingenuity.

For those who sometimes feel discouraged about the outlook for wilderness in a changing world, I will remind you that man is at his best and most creative when challenged.

In the course of the discussions that follow, noted authorities will focus on the challenges, and hopefully tell us how to meet them— including the challenge of an hallucinatory keynote address.

THE PRESSURE OF PEOPLE

↠ *Lincoln H. Day*

I have spent some very profitable hours recently, reading the proceedings of your three previous Wilderness Conferences. I find that those of you who have been attending these conferences have already been warned of the threat to wilderness inherent in the rapid population increase in this country. At the 1959 Conference, for example, Professor Raymond B. Cowles said:

> You have the pressures for lake fronts, stream sides, beach frontage, mountain property, anywhere there is beauty. These resources are as ample as they ever were, but not in terms of our present population size . . . underlying everything is our population size, again and again. *This is the basic factor.*

Four years later, at the 1963 Conference, nearly all of the speakers made some mention of the deleterious consequences arising from continued population growth. Professor Chauncey D. Leake said:

> . . . the major problem with which we have to contend, is simply that there are too many of us. . . .
> . . . It is population pressure that is basically responsible for the pollution of our airs and waters, for the increasing tensions in our everyday affairs, for producing the traffic snarls that are so annoying in our major cities, for despoiling the natural surroundings that all of us have prized so warmly, and for bringing so much of that governmental regulation that we hate and the bureaucracy that overwhelms us.

At that same conference Secretary Udall asked, "What will happen to the *quality* of life as we approach the point where the available natural areas of the continent offer standing room only?"

And he answered his own question in this manner:

> As population crowds in on us, it will surely be the quality experience that is sacrificed first—the kind of unique experience offered by wilderness. There will still be available the kind of outdoor experience that can be enjoyed today at amusement parks on the Fourth of July. And this may, indeed, be the *only* kind of outdoor experience available if we race blindly ahead down the road of 'growth and progress.'

I can only add my own misgivings to those expressed by these others. As a demographer, however, perhaps I can present you with a few additional considerations that might increase your understanding of both the magnitude of the problem and the challenge we face if we intend to meet it by action and not defeatism.

First, how does population growth actually operate to threaten the existence of wilderness? Statistics on numbers of visitors to our parks and recreation areas give only a small part of the picture. They tell us nothing of the *intensity* of use, nothing of the losses in *quality of experience* that additional visitors entail, nothing of the threats to these areas from air and water pollution, and from upsetting the balance of nature. Yet, for our purposes here, it is enough to note that the annual number of visitors to these areas has been increasing at a far faster rate than has the number of people in our population: in fact, at a rate about four times as fast. Even if by some miracle we were to halt population growth tomorrow, we could still expect substantial yearly increases in the numbers of visitors to these areas. Population is a sleeper, though: if there were no increase in the *proportion* of our people who availed themselves of these areas, population increase alone would double the number of users in but 45 more years. But if the current rates of increase in *both* population and usage continue, there will be a *doubling of the number of visitors in 10 more years*.

Now, apart from that portion due to population growth, this increase in use is a somewhat unfortunate consequence of a number of things that I think few of us would want to forego: for example, the extension of paid vacations, increases in buying power, and greater interest in the scenic and natural wonders of this country. What steadily encroaches on the sanctity of wilderness is rapid population growth *superimposed* on our American way of life.

The American population increased 18 percent in the decade just passed. This 18 percent increase would bring with it no corresponding increase in traffic jams, no overcrowding of vacation spots, no loss of land to roads and municipal facilities if only a few owned cars, or lived in suburbs, or had vacations. But with more than 360 private automobiles per 1,000 population; with three-fifths of our population living in the larger metropolitan centers, and half of these metropolitan dwellers living outside the central cities of these areas; with a probable majority of the work force enjoying annual paid vacations; and with ever greater demands for raw materials, rapid growth will inevitably increase the demand on wilderness—certainly for its recreational offerings, and probably also for its untapped resources of land, water, timber, and minerals. Unless Americans are prepared to reduce their material levels of living and to deny themselves certain of the privileges they now take for granted—such as freedom to travel any-where in this country, free and unlimited access to the public domain, and unrestricted car ownership—we can expect our increasing num-bers to produce a host of qualitative declines in the places available for our recreation. This process is already well underway.

What, then, are we to do about it? I think the situation calls for efforts to be made in at least four directions simultaneously. *First,* there needs to be even more pressure applied at the legislative and ex-ecutive branches of government. Preservation of these areas is, after all, a task to be achieved essentially through governmental means. *Second,* there needs to be more education of the public in the impor-tance of these areas, and especially in the proper care and appreciation of them. *Third,* our cities and their environs need to be made more liveable—socially, psychologically, esthetically. *Fourth,* and most basic of all, we must mobilize our efforts to halt the growth of popula-tion. There is also a fifth effort that could be made—one demanding far more extensive changes in our way of life than any of these others—and that is the expansion of those economic activities that make little or no use of non-renewable resources (such activities as health, edu-cation, care of the aged, parole and probation systems) and the corre-sponding contraction of those that make extensive demands on these resources (such as war, space exploration, automobile manufacture, and highway construction). An ambitious program, perhaps, but leave out any part of it, and the chance of achieving our ends is correspond-ingly diminished. Leave out the cessation of population growth and we may as well relinquish altogether our hopes for wilderness preser-vation over the long run.

In each of the first two activities, which involve public education, the Sierra Club already plays an active and highly important role. As far as the improvement of city living is concerned, there is room for much additional effort. Some of you may remember a few of the things Lawrence Halprin had to say on this point at the last Wilder-ness Conference:

> . . . I . . . propose that we . . . [differentiate] the true wilderness experience . . . from the need we all have to experience nature and be quiet at times on a woodland trail, or even to go fishing.
> These needs should be taken care of in our cities and our surroundings. If our cities were designed carefully to provide the kind of environment which we need,

then we could, in our daily rounds, lead creative lives without quite the urgency to relate to wilderness, except for the very special and unique qualities which only wilderness can bring.

If I may add to this, I think we are long past the time when the value of agriculture could be judged solely in terms of its economic function. Only seven percent of us now live on farms. Almost three-fourths of us live in cities, with over a third of us in urban concentrations of more than a million people. Some 80 percent of the population increase predicted for the next four decades is expected to come in the form of additional people in these metropolitan areas. Most of these areas are far removed from the more extensive outdoor recreational areas, much less true wilderness. It is time we recognized the importance of agriculture to conservation, to the control of pollution, and to recreation. Open space is essential to urban populations. In recognition of this, we must greatly extend zoning—certainly to cover the rural areas adjacent to our metropolitan centers. If this appears to be a loss of freedom, a denial of the American property owner's inalienable right to make a quick profit in real estate, I can only answer that it is but one of the milder losses of freedom we can expect to experience if our population continues to grow.

And this leads me to my fourth point: the need to check population growth—not just in China, not just in India, or Latin America, or Africa, but right here in the United States. Whatever we do with education and lobbying, whatever we do to curtail our voracious appetite for non-renewable resources, whatever we do with our cities or with rural zoning will come to naught unless we also achieve a cessation of our population growth. All other measures are but holding operations.

Now let's see just what this means. Each year we Americans add a number equal to the population of the whole San Francisco–Oakland urban area and nearly half a million larger than the entire Boston urban area, as we grow at a rate now capable of doubling our numbers every 45 years. We Americans need to count, and we need to think of our expanding numbers not as mere statistics but as additional Americans with whom we will need to share the resources of land, open space, water, recreational facilities, and social services now divided among a "mere" 193 million of us. It is not that we are threatened by a condition of "standing room only." Nor for a while, at least, are we presented with the prospect of losing possession of the world's highest *material* level of living.

What we stand to lose—and what to some extent we have already lost, as Secretary Udall pointed out—is to be reckoned essentially in *qualitative* terms. Superimposed on our high material level of living, rapid growth in the United States has already necessitated increasing control from external sources, less flexibility in behavior permitted the individual, greater centralization in government, rising economic costs, crowded schools and recreation areas, vanishing countryside, pollution of our air and water, endless traffic jams, and a steady loss in time, solitude, and peace of mind. This deterioration we are experiencing right now. Yet, half of us can expect to live long enough to see a time when, if present rates continue, we will number some 386 million and the difficulties attending population growth will have been increased and magnified by the fact of *two* Americans for every *one* here now.

We Americans are in a unique predicament with respect to our population size. We have already achieved extensive control over both mortality and natality. Our death rates are among the lowest in the world, while knowledge of how to prevent conception is, with us, nearly universal. Unlike the peoples of the rapidly growing nonindustrialized countries, we Americans already make extensive use of the most effective means of controlling birth to limit the size of our individual families. The average American couple of today has only about three children. The great majority of American families have no more than four.

The present situation in this country is thus a dramatic illustration of a new and tremendously significant fact: *no longer is the large family a requisite of population increase. The low mortality rates of today permit a rapid, sustained population growth when family size is of only modest dimensions.* Hence, the attainment of population stability by voluntary means is complicated in two important respects: first, the moderate size of the average family impedes public awareness of growth and widely diffuses responsibility for it; and second, with the typical family no larger than it is, *any further reduction in average family size can hardly come without entailing for many what may seem like a heavy personal sacrifice—the sacrifice of having fewer children than they want.*

The question, then, is this: will American couples voluntarily keep their procreation within replacement levels? To do so will mean settling for what is now considered quite a small family. With our low death rates there would be enough reproduction for replacement purposes if family size averaged only slightly more than two children per couple. This is not as unprecedented as it may sound. A number of countries have already approximated this condition: e.g., Japan, Belgium, Denmark, Luxembourg, Sweden, England, Austria, West Germany, Hungary, Switzerland, Bulgaria, Greece, Italy, and France. Several of these countries, incidentally, are overwhelmingly Catholic in religious affiliation: Belgium, Luxembourg, France, Austria, Hungary, and Italy. In this country, however, the family ideal of three or four children remains firmly entrenched, and Americans seem generally reluctant to consider the possibility that population size and growth rates are themselves factors contributing to the magnitude of our social problems.

There are, however, some signs of an emerging awareness. For one thing, the Johnson Administration seems determined to take precautions against further deterioration of a sort at least partly due to population growth: air and water pollution, the insufficiency of park and recreation areas, inadequate means of mass transportation, the shortage of educational facilities, mutilation of the countryside, and socially and esthetically inept city planning.

Moreover, as part of a so-called "anti-poverty" program, the Federal Government is now making funds available to a number of localities for the establishment and operation of birth control clinics. This is an important start. But let us not delude ourselves into thinking that the main cause of our numerical increase is excess reproduction among the poor or less educated. Differences in family size between income and educational categories have diminished considerably since World War II, and the trend toward closing this gap shows every indication of continuing. Yet, even at *current* rates, the middle and upper income and education groups are responsible for well over three-fourths of all births occurring in this country.

Improving the techniques of contraception and making them accessible might well work some reduction in our birth rate. But we will be making an important mistake if we put all our faith in techniques. Remember, with our low level of mortality and very high proportion of marriages, population in this country would still increase rapidly if the typical couple limited the number of its children to three. Moreover, recent studies of family size expectations (as distinguished from actual practice) show little variation at all between different income and education groups. The great majority of couples at all levels now want and expect to have at least three children. Thus, our rapid population increase derives hardly at all from *unwanted* children. It comes, instead, from those third, fourth, fifth children whose parents *want* them—or who are, at the very least, not *un*wanted enough for their parents to exercise sufficient care to prevent their conception or birth. During the Depression, with techniques of birth control less efficient than those available today, Americans succeeded in reducing their childbearing to a level just sufficient for replacement. Contraception is important; but it cannot do the job alone. It is motivation, not technique, that is the key to population control.

What then will motivate Americans to curtail their high rate of natural increase—to limit their families still further to but two, or at the very most, three children? I doubt if we can rely upon the facts of population pressure alone to provide this motivation. In no modern country that has achieved a demographic balance have declines in family size come as a conscious response to anxiety about the consequences of national population growth. These declines have come about instead as the response of individual couples to a social framework in which they felt that the bearing of more than two or three children would constitute a handicap in the achievement of personal goals and aspirations. I see no reason to suppose that American demographic behavior should be any more susceptible to such seemingly remote issues as the population-resources ratio, deterioration in the quality of life, or extermination of wilderness, although it is possible these appeals will become more effective as time goes on and the burdens attending population increase are experienced more acutely. (I wonder, for example, whether as the children of the post-war "baby boom" become parents, a measure of disillusionment over competition for jobs and higher education might not be reflected in lower birth rates.)

In pointing out that knowledge alone is an insufficient motivation for population control, I do not mean to imply that we should stand idly by and allow ourselves to become victimized by our runaway numbers. Awareness of the consequences of growth is certainly requisite to any extensive public concern over the present 2.6 million annual increment to our population. We need continuing education in the demographic facts of life: in the levels of natality and mortality and the trends in migration; and we need education in the meaning these hold for the quality of life in this country. Mass communications media, as well as schools and colleges, must help with this task.

In general, what we must work toward is a society in which no unwanted child is born; a society in which the decision to bear or not to bear a child is made solely by the potential parents; and most importantly, a society in which decisions about childbearing are made in a social and cultural context in which a family of three children is defined as large. As in other populations that have achieved this degree of control over their numbers, this would be a society in which couples limited their families to but two children because that was the accepted pattern of behavior—the "natural" thing to do.

We need, in short, to alter the image of what constitutes the "ideal" American family, and to point out why the bearing of a large family can no longer be construed as a social contribution. In fact, if our rate of increase continues high, it will become necessary to be even blunter by pointing out that those who elect to have more than the two—or at the very most, three—children necessary for replacement are indulging themselves at the expense of the rest of the society. And this will have to be impressed upon people at *all* levels of our society. For if we are honest with ourselves, we must admit that when it comes to wilderness preservation (and many other things we value in our way of life), the excess reproduction of the privileged is in many respects just as burdensome as that of the poor—if not more so. The style of life of the privileged, with its extra car, its lakeshore cottage, its larger property, greater amounts of travel, and generally more material possessions, requires a much higher consumption of those very things upon which population increase—in whatever class—places a premium: raw materials and space. Bringing it right down to the matter at hand, is it not, after all, the families of the middle and upper income categories who make up the great bulk of visitors to wilderness areas, who threaten the existence of these areas by their wide-ranging recreational activities and their high material expectations? The families of the poor remain economically—and often psychologically—penned in their slums.

In conclusion, let me reiterate my belief that population stability must soon be achieved if we Americans are to maintain for ourselves and bequeath to our posterity any measure of a high quality of life as we now know it. This includes, of course, the luxury of access to undeveloped open lands. There is no dearth of proposals which, if put into effect, would help maintain—and possibly, for a while, even improve—the quality of life in this country. But in the absence of a check on our population growth, these proposals are short-term measures at best. They are palliatives, not cures.

COMPREHENSIVE PLANNING
AND THE DRAGON TO SLAY

> ⋙ *Luna B. Leopold*

Several years ago I was in India as consultant to that Government concerning a flood-control project on the Kosi River in the State of Bihar. The Kosi originates near Mount Everest and emerges from the Himalayas to flow southward for nearly a hundred miles across the Ganges plain. It is a braided river with an ill-defined channel consisting of many distributaries wandering around myriad islands in an unsystematic way. Owing to the fact that the Kosi has moved laterally across its low-angle fan about 75 miles in a hundred years, it has progressively devastated, by flooding, large areas of agricultural land.

The Indian Government had chosen as the most practical way to alleviate the flood damage the construction of levees separated by a distance of about 9 miles and confining the river through most of its course across the plain.

We were invited to the office of the Commissioner [comparable to a state governor here] who wished to discuss with us the philosophy of this flood-control plan. He said, "As you can imagine, with levees so far apart, a situation made necessary by the large width taken up by the many channels of the Kosi, there are many local residents whose homes and fields are being included within the area confined between the levees. Do you think that this Government has incurred an obligation to these people to resettle them from their present location at Government expense to some other land outside of the confines of the levees?" My immediate answer was in the affirmative. I argued that before the levees were built the people had lived on the land at considerable risk of damage by the river in flood, but once the levees were built their exposure to flood was assured.

I said I thought the obligation was of such a nature that the people ought to be moved even before the levee system were completed. "I fear you cannot appreciate the problem," he said. "Not only do we have no other lands to which these people can be moved, but also there are many people confined within the levees." How many, I asked. His answer was, "More than a quarter of a million."

In the United States the professionals concerned with water-development planning have grown accustomed to believe that there is no problem for which a technical solution cannot be found. This being the case, one can approach every planning problem in terms of finding an engineering solution which has the highest ratio of benefit to cost. The human or social aspects involved, that is the non-monetary aspects, are usually either turned into monetary values or mentioned in a few paragraphs and thenceforth disregarded.

Because most of our basic legislation governing the expenditure of Federal money does not explicitly define what is meant by a benefit and what is meant by a cost, it has been necessary to evolve through actual experience ways of evaluating benefits that lend themselves to a final computation of a benefit-cost ratio. There is a philosophic assumption underlying such practice, that the indirect or the non-monetary benefits and costs, though important, are unusable in making the final determination of whether a development scheme is or is not justified.

There has grown up, therefore, the practice of computing by different means price-tags that purport to measure the value even of those gains and losses that do not lend themselves well to this type of description. Seldom are we faced with social costs on such a massive scale as the Kosi example. Such costs or gains are generally either too obscure or too far removed in time to be determining factors in whether a given development plan is to be considered or discarded.

In the early days of water development in the United States the possible alternatives in any development were relatively wide. The demand for water relative to its availability was not so great that competition was very intense. There were available alternative dam sites and alternative land suitable for development. The total encroachment of water-development works was not yet severe. With time the alternatives have become fewer. The best projects have already been built, and the economic as well as the social justification is far less clear than it had been in previous decades.

It was then that the dragon's teeth were sown. It was the promotion of water projects that led to the introduction of the benefit-cost economics in public affairs. Benefit-cost ratios are not traditional in other aspects of public works. None considered it necessary to so evaluate schools, roads, post offices, police, and other facilities and services. These things are argued in terms of the satisfaction they yielded to the public—not what they return only in the way of dollars. We have reaped the dragon's teeth by extension of benefit-cost economics into esthetics.

There developed, simultaneously, a concept of multiple use based on the idea that where two uses could be served by a development rather than one, the resource would be more efficiently utilized and more benefits could be obtained for each unit of cost. This concept was reinforced by the practical-engineer truism that the unit cost of a large project is lower than the unit cost of a small one. Multi-purpose use, therefore, became not only a supporting argument but also tended to be looked upon as the measure of efficiency of resource utilization.

The concept of multiple use can be handled at the planning level only by the involvement of a variety of disciplines because specialists in each type of use are required in the planning and in the evaluation process. This interdisciplinary approach has forced the managers of esthetic and non-monetary social values to place a dollar cost on these values. Interdisciplinary water-development plans are transmitted for comment to all interested agencies. Disagreement with any aspect of a proposed development is then usually handled within the bureaus involved, and the final product is often advertised as a joint plan involving many, if not all, of the concerned government agencies. In reality such a joint plan does not necessarily indicate what the several bureaus concerned would actually recommend individually. The portions dealing with scenic and non-economic resources usually represent merely a proposal concerning how best to accept or live with the proposed engineering works.

Such cooperative planning requires that evaluations of all aspects be set forth in terms which would be mutually compatible. In practical terms this means that various interests are expressed in monetary terms or they would, in fact, have no appreciable impact on the proposed program.

For example, it became necessary to evaluate the benefits and costs to fish and wildlife in the same terms that are used to describe the benefits and costs of flood control or of irrigation. The difficult technical problem posed is an assessment of how a given development would adversely or beneficially affect not only the hunting possibilities for migratory waterfowl but also the breeding and resting habitats of non-migratory and therefore immoveable species. It may necessitate an evaluation of the difference in worth between trout and bluegills, or between salmon and non-salmon. The results of these evaluations are known to all. The benefit to fish and wildlife is expressed in terms of the tonnage of fish taken, or the commercial value of the visitor day. The esthetic value of having trout in a reach of river, whether or not it adds tonnage to the creel, becomes a non-monetary benefit or cost and because it is non-monetary, it is essentially discarded.

The net result was that a value was placed on an individual duck in terms of its worth in a game bag. Interestingly, a mallard by this process became worth $2.00, and a goose worth $6.00. The more difficult problem of evaluating other kinds of recreation that do not have a take or bag was relegated to the formula of the visitor day.

Clearly there is an economic value to the society from the expenditure of time and money by individuals engaged in recreation. The recreationist spends money for gasoline, food, lodging, boat rental, camera equipment, skis, and the like. Though it is desirable to recognize the economic worth of the activities of the recreationist, there is practical as well as philosophic cause for alarm at the implication that the value of recreation lies in the expenditure for equipment rather than on the quality of the recreational experience.

The evaluation of recreation in terms of the visitor day is the assertion that two recreationists are twice as valuable as one, and therefore a hundred recreationists are a hundred times more valuable. Social values deny this type of reasoning.

It is generally supposed that a development plan is necessarily better if it is multi-purpose and comprehensive than if it is single-purpose and of local application. Multi-purpose planning means in practice that individual portions of a development scheme need not necessarily satisfy the requirements that the individual benefits exceed the individual costs. The whole may be justified as long as the complex of development yields a net monetary benefit exceeding the net cost.

Costs and benefits in this context mean economic and therefore tangible benefits and costs. The comprehensive plan tends to incorporate even a wider variety of affected uses than individual multi-purpose projects, for when a whole region is encompassed in a comprehensive plan, then a still wider diversity of people and situations is encompassed than would be in a single multi-purpose project.

The fact that such a variety of aspects may in reality introduce competition rather than symbiosis has not tarnished the value of the word comprehensive. The comprehensive plan can be potentially even more erosive to the esthetic and non-monetary values than a single multi-purpose project, owing to its much larger affect on the landscape and environment.

What the long-term effect is on society, for good or bad, of a comprehensive resource plan is difficult to judge because the social benefits and social costs are more dispersed that where a quarter of a million people are enclosed between levees.

There is another danger in the present scheme of monetary evaluation. The benefit-cost type of reasoning carries with it the implicit assertion that society is best served by developing not merely within the present generation, but immediately, all of the resources the monetary benefits of which can be demonstrated to exceed the costs. One may ask what is the cost of the resultant reduction in flexibility of choice left for future generations. Yet the concept of a comprehensive river basin plan is supposed to be our assurance that such a social cost is not significant.

Our knowledge of science outpaces the development of ethical principles. The newer the knowledge, the greener the ethics. Only recently have we learned that bigness is the way to economic efficiency. We have come to believe that bigness in the market place is not only compatible with but necessary for quality. Long highways are better than side roads. Big universities offer better graduate schools than country colleges.

Markets attest to the merit of the economies of scale. The same idea is behind the multi-purpose and multi-basin water plans. They began only yesterday, so to speak, at first combining only irrigation and power, as at Boulder Dam, and then becoming basinwide, and now we are soon to consider a scheme that stretches from Alaska to Mexico and puts New York and California on the same pipeline.

These proposals will be argued about chiefly in the benefit-cost framework. But the speed with which we improve our econometrics and our construction methods out-runs the enlargement of our ethical attitude toward landscape. In the process, bigness can subvert quality. Assigning dollar values to irrigation and power is one matter; assuming that all recreation can be measured in similar terms is another.

The emphasis on least cost as it is presently interpreted does not provide society with an adequate choice. Society may well choose, if given an opportunity, a development scheme which is higher in immediate dollar cost than an alternative, but that would preserve some natural asset.

Let us examine in more detail the nature of the gain in efficiency in multi-purpose over single-purpose structures. The advantage to be gained by combining in a single dam, for example, the primary purposes of flood control and irrigation, comes primarily from the fact that per unit of reservoir volume the cost is lower for a large dam than for a small one. This may not be the undertanding gained by the public, who probably think that the same storage capacity can be used for each of the two purposes. For irrigation or municipal use the storage must be utilized during times of high flow and depleted during times of low flow. For flood control on the other hand, storage must be depleted at all times in order that when a high flow occurs it can be utilized. So a reservoir for water supply should be kept as full as possible and one for flood control as empty as possible. The same storage volume cannot be used simultaneously for both purposes at the same time.

A given amount of water discharge through a penstock develops more power under a high head than under a low one. Therefore, from the standpoint of power production, the more depth in a reservoir the better. Also one of the advantages of hydroelectric power production is that by merely opening or closing the penstocks, the rate of power generation can be adjusted rapidly to meet variations in demand. For this reason hydro-power is considered to be especially efficient for peaking purposes.

In contrast to all these uses, reservoir operation for recreation is most efficient when the water level is kept as steady as possible, with minimum fluctuations. It can be seen, therefore, that in principle, preferences for various reservoir uses are completely in conflict.

What is truly meant by the recreational use of a reservoir built for water supply, flood control, or power generation is that during the time a body of water exists it can sustain fish or float a boat. Any more sophisticated value of the water for recreation is made subservient to the alternative engineering purposes.

To summarize, then, a so-called multi-purpose reservoir does not mean that the same storage can be used for more than one purpose, except collaterally or by chance. Multi-purpose development merely means that the cost of each unit of storage decreases as the height of the dam increases.

Exactly the same kinds of conflict appear, in principle, in other kinds of multi-purpose use. Selective logging may, by opening up the stand, increase the forage production for grazing. Weighed against this is the ever-present possibility that in certain ecological types, an incursion of brush or other less desirable species may negate hope for improvement in total forage capacity. Whereas the expansion of agriculture materially improved game-bird and animal production in certain ecological types over that which had existed in the virgin state, this increased productivity generally resulted from the increase in the linear extent of edges between two vegetative types in juxtaposition. Thus, it cannot be said always that either logging or grazing will necessarily improve the production of game-birds and animals.

The relation between logging, grazing, and recreation is somewhat less clear because the criteria governing recreational uses are less clear than those measuring the productivity of lumber, wool, or beef. The only thing that is obvious is that for wilderness recreation any regular utilization is detrimental. There is a big enough problem in learning how to manage wilderness lands in order to keep the biota stable, but a clear distinction should be drawn between the management of lands for long-term stability and the regular utilization of that land for economic production.

In my opinion, then, multiple use has become a shibboleth tending to obscure the actual benefits to society, because losses and gains to society are both economic and non-monetary. Presumably before any alternative philosophy can be given serious consideration, it is vitally necessary that a larger segment of the public recognize the difference between the true economies to be obtained by multi-purpose development and the unreality which has grown in the public mind that multi-purpose development is a good thing per se. In present planning procedures, non-development is not considered as a real alternative. Immediate development is considered the only valid aim, and one to be recommended as soon as it can be shown that monetary benefit exceeds cost.

I am convinced that the non-monetary and esthetic values of the landscape can never be preserved if their economic significance is pitted against that of engineering works. It seems necessary to divide resource planning into two steps.

In the first stage, there should be presented to the public in equal detail the alternative schemes by which the stated objectives could be achieved. The public deserves to be informed of the various ways development might be approached. They should be offered for consideration and discussion more than merely what some planner considers to be the "best scheme," and more than what some economist computes to be the "least cost" plan. When given the alternatives, the public increasingly is known to prefer some plan other than that carrying the lowest dollar price tag.

The first stage should illuminate those esthetic and non-monetary values in landscape or in resources that should not be called upon to face a test of monetary significance. Those of greatest social value would be identified and, through a process analogous to zoning, would be set aside for preservation and non-development.

In the second stage, the hard-boiled economic realities of all those resources not marked for preservation should be weighed in a far more sophisticated manner than is now practiced in order that the most efficient engineering and technological design for their development be achieved.

For the second stage the present simple comparison of so-called benefits and costs should be up-dated and elaborated to a level that would utilize economic knowledge and theory already extant and that would make the economic design somewhere near the level of sophistication that characterizes the engineering technology.

I believe there exists a social value in maintaining and enhancing the quality of landscape. There is an esthetic uplift to be gained in a deeper concern for the world in which we have to live. But in our path is a dragon which regenerates itself every time it suffers attack. The dragon of misconception concerning the planning process is ever enlarging its radius of use. We must arm ourselves with the moral conviction that the cost to society of present procedures is too large, and that we must attack the dragon on its own ground before there is nothing more left for us to protect.

THE ECONOMIC ASPECTS
OF CONSERVATION

⋙ *John B. Condliffe*

For some months now, under the gentle but persistent prodding of Mrs. Wayburn, I have been pursuing a refresher course on the literature of wilderness. This has been a pleasant but frustrating experience. There are no adjectives that have not already been used in eloquent praise of wilderness and what it means to man. I have enjoyed taking John Muir off the shelf again. I agree, as we all do, with almost everything that has been said so eloquently and so passionately at these conferences by so many nature lovers. I read the *Sierra Club Bulletin* faithfully and I write to my Congressman—who tells me that he couldn't agree with me more. Harold Gilliam's articles are a joy to me. But I get the impression that no one disagrees with us in principle. Everyone loves the wilderness—even those who are busy destroying it.

The very success of the conservation cause contributes to its difficulties. My wife and I have ten grandchildren. All of them are ardent trout fishermen, skiers, and would-be climbers. Lest you think I am boasting, let me remind you that on his 83rd birthday last summer, Joel Hildebrand led eighteen of his tribe to a mountain top in the Sierra. Whenever we send out those lovely Sierra Club books—as birthday or Christmas gifts or just to pay a special debt of gratitude —we recruit more wilderness lovers. So the demand for wilderness grows. And if I may lapse into economic language, this demand is inelastic. Those who have once seen the eloquent light are forever haunted by it.

We are just at the beginning of this inelastic demand. There will be more people, many more, especially in California. More of them will want to escape to the wilderness and will have the means to do so. Later, I shall try to pick up Catherine Bauer Wurster's argument that the center of our problem is in the cities, not on the mountain tops. But first I want to register the fact that in the face of this exponential demand, doubling and redoubling in size and intensity from generation to generation, we cannot afford to restrict the supply of wilderness. Alas, we cannot add to it. The supply is not just inelastic. It is fixed. No matter how high you raise the price of admission to the national parks, you can't increase the supply. So it is imperative that, whatever arguments are thrust upon us, we fight tenaciously to save every scrap of wilderness left to us—every stand of redwoods, every yard of foreshore, every marsh and mud-flat around San Francisco Bay. Once gone, it is gone forever.

Linnie Marsh Wolfe quoted a phrase from John Muir's autobiographical fragments that has intrigued me since I first read it. He described the laissez-faire beliefs of his day as "the gobble-gobble school of economics." I have not yet been able to track down these autobiographical fragments, but I think I know now where they are, if they still exist. They should be rescued and used as a basis for analysis of what is really the heart of our problem. Not having seen them, I do not know whether it was John Muir or Mrs. Wolfe who pinned the "gobble-gobble" doctrine on to Adam Smith, who did not in fact endorse competition as the law of the universe. He would not have endorsed a great deal of the wanton destruction that his authority was later invoked to justify.

I have said that this is the heart of our problem because it is essentially an economic problem—the choice of the best use to be made of scarce resources. Another great economist, Alfred Marshall, has emphasized the fact, too often forgotten by idealists, that social reform depends on being able to enlist not only the highest, but the strongest, motives of human behavior. We can be eloquent about the beauty of nature and the healing power of solitude. But if we are to preserve the wilderness against encroachments we must also be prepared to show that these encroachments are destructive not only of beauty but of economic values.

Later I shall comment on some of the peculiar calculations that enter into so-called highway economics—the benefit-cost calculation, as Dr. Luna Leopold called them. I hope to convince you that we ought not to be intimidated by them. But I do not want anyone to think I am picking on the engineers. Mrs. Wayburn gave me 25 minutes and warned me that it was the absolute limit. So if I am not to be cut off in mid-sentence before I have done justice to the highway engineers, I must content myself with saying that, in my judgment, you ought not to concede the economic argument to the developers. Indeed it might be worthwhile to employ a competent economic analyst to study these questions from the conservation point of view. It would also be worthwhile to study the tax system that is taking so much good agricultural land out of cultivation and threatens to destroy the California wine industry. Indeed I believe the conservation movement ought to use economists at least as much as the developers and engineers do. The founder of an earlier conservationist movement—the Salvation Army—was once reproached for using a ribald drinking tune to which Gospel words had been set. General Booth's reply to his critic was that there was no reason to let the devil have all the good tunes.

Too often we think of this problem only in terms of remote areas to which we can escape from the congested and unnatural living conditions of our great cities. But this is all one problem. There are now four million people living around the Bay. The Conservation Study Commission that has just reported to the California State Legislature estimates that in the year 2020 there may be not 4 but 14 million people living around San Francisco Bay. What will this mean in terms of housing, of streets and highways, factories and shopping centers, theaters and galleries, automobiles and trucks, air space and landing fields, parks and beaches, schools and playing fields, foul air and polluted water? Unless we begin very soon to bring some overriding authority to bear on the clutter of village governments and regional boards that govern the Bay Area, it is not difficult to imagine the vast extension of ticky-tacky suburban developments across the hilltops, if there are any hilltops left, and over the water until the Bay is reduced to a dirty drainage channel with bridges crossing in every direction. The idea of forming these bridges into inter-connected traffic junctions will certainly commend itself to our highway engineers. They may even try to put a concrete roof over what is left of the Bay and make a landing field out of it.

One of the keys to this situation is control of the watersheds in the Bay Area. These are under the control of the local water districts. The men who control these boards pride themselves on keeping down the price of water, which is very cheap in the Bay Area. There is real danger that in order to keep down the price, they may sell off bits and pieces of these watershed areas. In fact, they are already doing so. There is a stretch of open country around the San Pablo Dam just beyond the East Bay's Tilden Park which is being nibbled at right now. If we are not careful, we may wake up some day to find that we have lost not only the salt water in the Bay, but the fresh-water catchment areas all around it.

Can anyone believe that we shall be able to keep the coastline and the Sierra from being sacrificed to the developers if we do not pre-serve these open spaces and begin now to set aside recreation centers in the urban areas and the surrounding suburban and ex-urban com-munities? To do this will involve much more than our present tinker-ing with city-planning on a fragmentary and piecemeal basis.

My argument is not new. When Alfred Marshall published the first edition of his *Principles of Economics* in 1890, he summed up his views on production costs by arguing that increased population and increased production generally brought improved living standards and greater social welfare. He had only one qualification (to take care of the Malthusian risk)—welfare would be increased, provided an ade-quate supply of raw produce could be obtained without great diffi-culty. But in his second edition published a year later, in 1891, and maintained through all subsequent editions, he added a second qualifi-cation: that there must be "no such overcrowding as causes physical and moral vigour to be impaired by the want of fresh air and light and of healthy and joyous recreation for the young."

Marshall recognized that the range of economic analysis would ex-tend beyond those facts that can be measured objectively in money. As more information becomes available and analytical techniques im-prove, economists make efforts to measure the imponderables of social choice that Marshall recognized but felt had not yet become measura-ble. There is a growing literature of welfare theory, still more easily applied to money than to esthetic values, but beginning to be extended experimentally to such imponderables as we are concerned with. It seems quite certain that there will be rapid advances in the analysis of social choices and their relation to individual values. There is no doubt in my mind that this will lead to greater acceptance of the ne-cessity to preserve social amenities even at the cost of some expansion of the public sector of the economy and some curtailment of individual economic freedom. This is not new. We don't allow individuals or in-dustries to run sewage into our collective water supply. Why should we allow them to wreck our remaining open spaces?

Here in the United States and in all the advanced industrial countries, the Malthusian problem has been overtaken by the progress of applied science. Our problem is not food and material shortages, but surpluses. Indeed a good argument could be made that the national economy could be improved and the gross national product increased if we could eliminate or greatly reduce the burden of maintaining agricultural prices at their present levels. This would force the abandonment of much uneconomic production and accelerate the reduction of the agricultural population which has been going on for several decades. And we should all benefit both from lower food prices and from lower taxes. From the conservationist's viewpoint, we could prevent much erosion of range lands if we also took the tariff off wool and allowed beef to be imported without quota limits. The same argument could be made for removing the quotas and excise taxes that hinder the imports of minerals and petroleum. Incidentally, this would be a greater help to the underdeveloped countries than the billions of dollars of economic aid that we tax ourselves to provide. As taxpayers and as consumers, we should all be better off. The gain to the economy as a whole would be far greater than the losses that would be sustained by domestic producers. Indeed it would pay the United States to buy out the interests of these producers and turn the land on which they operate into national parks. You may think this is just the old free-trade argument which is said to be politically impractical. And so it is. But whether such a policy could be implemented or not, we should be clear that there is no economic case for preserving these industries at the expense of the national economy. The profit to an individual from such a protected industry ought not to be confused with its social benefits. The nation is poorer because we keep these uneconomic industries going at the expense of the taxpayer and the consumer.

Essentially the same argument can be made concerning the economic cost of providing the necessary facilities for recreation and health, including the preservation of wilderness. When the highway engineers or the port engineers brush aside pleas for the preservation of irreplaceable natural beauty, their calculations are too narrow on three counts.

In the first place they confine their calculations to specific items of construction rather than the whole system. Secondly, they consider only the material costs. And, even more important, their time horizon is too short—they do not think far enough into the future.

I do not pretend to be an expert on engineering economics, but I have looked through the report of a Highway Workshop Conference published by no less august a body than the National Research Council of the National Academy of Sciences.*

All the papers and discussions were on highway economics. Quite early I came across some surprising statements. There was, for example, the classification (by an eminent public servant) of the factors to be considered in analyzing a proposed highway facility. They fell into five categories.

The first was consumption or conservation of physical goods and natural resources. This doesn't mean what you or I might think it might mean. The main items considered here were motor vehicle running costs and goods consumed because of accidents.

The second category was the use of time by individuals. Both these categories were said to be easily convertible into dollar values.

Next came the effect of a highway on the values of adjoining property, goods, and services—mainly land values.

The fourth category consisted of the mental and physical condition of the traveler. These were said to be intangible and without any evidence as to their monetary worth. Nevertheless, they were estimated and estimated quite highly.

Not so with the final group of factors which bore the title, "Other factors, preferably not included in the solution." Let me read the list—"social life, environment, political organization, esthetics, recreation, pleasures, scenic view, and other intangibles."

These factors, we are told, "are best considered as extra-market consequences, outside the economic analysis and given such weight as may be just and right in each case, by those officials who have final responsibility for approval of improvement projects."

This statement is worth considering in some detail. Notice first that final responsibility for decisions is allotted to officials. We in California know what this means. Who are these officials? Are they the appointed Highway Engineers? What right have they to decide what weight ought to be given to our social life, environment, political organization, esthetics, recreation, pleasures, scenic view, and other in-

---

* Highway Research Board, Special Report 56, "Economic Analysis in Highway Programming, Location and Design," Workshop Conference Proceedings, Sept. 17–18, 1959, National Academy of Sciences–National Research Council, Publication 775.

tangibles? Or are they the politicians we elect? I'm in favor of the politicians. With them at least we have a chance. When an old friend of mine was first appointed Minister of Transport in New Zealand, he received in succession two deputations on the subject of gasoline taxes. The first was from the County Councils who wanted money for roads. The second was from the Automobile Association. He was naïve enough to tell the second deputation that he couldn't make up his mind on this economic question because he wasn't sure which side had the most votes. It's up to us to see that our politicians do not doubt that we have the most votes.

I was interested not only in what the engineers leave out of their calculations, but in what they put in. Let me quote one example that was spelled out in detail. In the engineer's own words, "the improved highway may reduce motor vehicle running cost by one cent a vehicle-mile. As an added factor, if 0.5 cent per mile is allowed for comfort and convenience, the benefits are thus increased by 50 percent. Similarly, if $1.50 an hour is taken as the value of time as compared to $1.00 an hour, the benefits of time saved are increased 50 percent."

In the example given, the benefits of the new road are calculated as consisting 84.4 percent in the value of time saved, and 11.5 percent in the value attributed to comfort and convenience. The remaining 4.1 percent is the saving on automobile wear and tear. I find these estimates staggering, even in a hypothetical example, but what really is significant is the statement that "most any quantitative answer can be obtained if one desires to manipulate these factors within their minimum and maximum values." This surprising confession is illustrated by numerical examples following which the engineers are warned that "too often the critical factors of time, personal comfort, interest rate, and period of analysis are chosen without serious consideration of their effect on the final answer." I don't know any economist who would tell his colleagues that if they wanted their calculations to come out right, they must be careful to choose the right numbers.

Actually in the scarcity situation with a fixed supply of wilderness and inelastic demand for it, the value approximates to infinity. There is no way to price a painting by an old master except by the desire of collectors to own it. If we put in a proper value on the cost of destroying wilderness, no social benefit would justify building a freeway through the redwoods. What benefits does a freeway bring? The cost of the concrete is far more than the saving on automobile wear and tear, so those who promote this freeway are driven to justify it by telling us how valuable the time is that we save by traveling faster. This is over 84 percent of the benefit. For good measure, they throw in 11 percent as the value of comfort and convenience (and I presume peace of mind) we get from traveling faster on the freeways. So, in fact, the destruction of the redwoods is justified primarily by the time saved in driving through them.

It seems clear to me that we do not have to believe what the engineers tell us about highway construction costs and benefits. The fact is that they can calculate the cost of the concrete and the saving on automobile wear and tear. They cannot calculate the far more important cost of destroying the wilderness and therefore they ignore it.

I am not against freeways. I use them all the time. But I don't feel I have to accept these engineering calculations of their costs and benefits, and so I don't believe the argument that for economic reasons the freeways must go where the engineers find it easiest to lay the concrete. Nor do I feel ready to allow them to value what the scenery is worth to me and to you. I'm afraid that if they have their way unchecked, there won't be any scenery. In any case we go so fast along the freeways that it is as much as your life is worth to take your eyes off the road ahead. As John Steinbeck says, you can travel all across America and never see it.

It is an encouraging fact that the great business corporations are beginning to take much broader views. In the location of their industrial plants, in their architecture, including the landscaping and in the provision of access and space, they are taking into account the needs not only of the enterprise as a whole, but also of the community it serves and of the future. They are cost-conscious, but they do not make the mistake of choosing pinch-penny solutions to minimize immediate costs of a particular operation at the expense of everybody else. And they have learned that it pays in the long run to provide both their workers and their customers with agreeable surroundings and easy access to their homes. There are some corporations that take care to provide or assist in the provision of adequate and convenient outdoor recreation facilities for their staffs. Not all corporations are so farsighted. There are some who would not hesitate to destroy bits of the wilderness, but the trend now runs the other way.

It might be expected that public servants who are appointed to serve the interests not of particular groups, but of the whole community, would be even more concerned with the social costs and benefits of their construction activities. But in fact much damage is being done to the wilderness by those we employ to serve the public interest. That they do not pay more attention to overall planning based on adequate research, to the non-material costs of their operations, and to their long-range effects requires some explanation. In large part, I suspect, the explanation lies in the political processes through which they must work. The public servant is always under investigation and audit, and dare not risk bold and imaginative decisions that can be criticized as extravagant and impractical. He is always under pressure for results, and at the lowest cost. The sources of state and local body funds are derived from direct taxes that bear harshly on particular groups of property owners. There are always political pressures for immediate action.

It is not my intention to suggest that our public servants are inefficient or insensitive to community needs. It is not the individuals but the system that can be criticized when comparisons are drawn with private industry. But it is my intention to suggest that in the fight to preserve what is left of the wilderness, we should not be intimidated by the narrow cost considerations and inflated appreciation of time-saving with which we are so often confronted. If account is taken of the long-run social costs and benefits to the community as a whole, the economics of the argument are on our side, not on the side of highway engineers or those who would fill up San Francisco Bay. If we accept the narrow view, we ignore the price that future generations will have to pay in health and mental strain, in traffic congestion and accidents, in the ever-increasing costs of pulling down city freeways that should never have been built where they are, and in all the enormous costs of delay and frustration. We may not be able to put a dollar value on the cost of depriving those who come after us of the priceless heritage that has been ours, but I for one do not want my grandchildren and their children to lose that heritage because in our generation we took such a narrow, materialistic, and short-sighted view that we could not appraise the wilderness at its true value.

Courtesy of the California Division of Highways

Freeways, Highways, and Scenic Values

"THE TIME is fast approaching for a new look at freeways. The individual
battles rage on and the real question, more often than not, escapes notice.
Is the freeway the solution to the transportation problem it has been
thought to be, or is the freeway now the problem? . . ."—DAVID BROWER

*Where should freeways lead? Not through parks where natural values are high.
Even in our cities, what is the role of the freeway?*

Old highway through the Humboldt Redwoods State Park   *Photo from* The Last Redwood

Some roads let us see trees;
others take us through at high speeds;
only leisurely display roads belong in areas of high scenic quality.

Freeway through
Humboldt Redwoods
State Park
from The Last Redwoods

"The old highway almost tunnels through the forest, opening a mini-mum rift in the canopy overhead. It does no violence to the harmony of the landscape. . . . The freeway is something else again. A four-lane, high-speed structure with a minimum of curves and grades, it cuts a brutal swath through the trees. In places the slopes were gouged to many times the freeway's width with cuts and fills to prevent landslides."

—*The Last Redwoods*

Philip Hyde

"Preserved for all time" is a phrase that Americans feel can be applied to all state and national parks. Yet plans of our highway departments pose great threats to this illusion. Unusual scenery should come first in these areas; high speeds are unnecessary. The plan and profile of the highway can be flexible, with cuts and fills minimized.

*Photo by
David Brower*

National Park Service

The total width of scenic alteration should be kept to a minimum, as was accomplished (above) by use of a retaining wall. Lack of consideration of this matter (below) resulted in 110 feet of disturbance—including 50 feet of spill below the road.

*Photo by
David Brower*

New freeway through Founder's Grove at Humboldt Redwoods State Park, with the old highway to the left, difficult to see even from the air. Photograph by Philip Hyde.

The old and new Tioga Road in Yosemite National Park, California. Photograph by Robin Welch.

Photo by
Harold Bradley

*The road can bend more easily
than the scenery.*

"It seems clear to me that we do not have to believe what the engineers tell us about highway construction costs and benefits. The fact is that they can calculate the cost of the concrete and the saving on automobile wear and tear. They cannot calculate the far more important cost of destroying the wilderness, and therefore they ignore it.

"What benefits does a freeway bring? The cost of the concrete is far more than the saving on automobile wear and tear, so those who promote the freeway are driven to justify it by telling us how valuable the time is that we save by traveling faster."—JOHN CONDLIFFE

POINT REYES

MT. TAMALPAIS

BOLINAS LAGOON
STINSON BEACH

MUIR BEACH

HIGHWAY

GOLDEN GATE BRIDGE

A plan which continues to be considered by California's Division of Highways would place another north-south freeway (white line) through Marin County, across some of its most scenic coastline country. Aerial photograph by Aero Photographers, Sausalito.

"We can't afford to have every man require a ton of steel to drive himself from his bed to his desk, and 300 square feet of concrete to park it at either end . . . . Everywhere you look, now or in your mind's eye a decade from now, you see the blasting at work, the earth movers, the massive disruptions of natural beauty and civic beauty that might be acceptable if they really solved the problem. But they do not. They erode, instead, the financial feasibility of other transportation solutions that could really move people instead of just moving an ever-increasing number of vehicles."—DAVID BROWER

FROM THE DISCUSSION

William E. Siri, Lincoln H. Day, Luna B. Leopold, John B. Condliffe, David Brower

⋙ *James P. Gilligan, Chairman*

MR. DAVID BROWER: I am very grateful to Will Siri for what he did and for the stimulating prediction—the horribly stimulating prediction—he gave of the period 100 years from now. I like the phrase he gave us, "the confused sense of achievement," and I think if there is anything we in the wilderness movement are trying to attack or trying to correct, it is this confused sense of achievement.

I agree with him very much that man is at his best when challenged: the motivational study on the Mount Everest expedition, of which Will Siri was deputy leader, finds that motivation is greatest also when one is uncertain. In other words, one should be wary of the *certain* man; you don't have to worry about me.

I am very grateful to Dr. Day for putting the vital foundation under this conference—a good look at the population problem, and how impossible it is going to be for people to take care of the problems that people make if there are too many people.

I am also grateful to Luna Leopold, as I knew I would be, for his careful look at the economics of engineering—especially, as I read between the lines, the engineering of dams. I know this is particularly pertinent to us as we enter one of the big struggles this year—the attempt to keep dams out of Grand Canyon.

And I am grateful to Dr. Condliffe for his similarly hard look at the economics of the highway engineers. I hope we can take full advantage of his offer to get more economists working for us. I will be down there knocking at his door, so I can find out what I should find out to tell you to write your Congressman about. Having said that, I have just a few notes of my own. I want to take advantage of one of Dan Luten's illustrations (I can, because I have the platform and he doesn't). Dr. Luten has been one of my coaches on population matters, even as Howard Zahniser was my coach on practically everything else I know of conservation, a coach I miss very much today.

The other day Dr. Luten asked me to imagine a whole series of encyclopedia volumes, about the size of the *Britannica*. Let each word on each page of a thousand-page volume be a year. A thousand years per page, a thousand pages to the volume, and let the time of life be represented by the requisite number of volumes—that comes out to about 2,000, so that volume one would be behind me and the series would go completely around this room. Halfway through the next to the last volume, man appeared on earth. Then turn to the last volume: 300 pages from the end of that last volume is the page on which man was learning how to use a tool, a shaped stone; for nearly 300,000 years that was about the only tool he used, that, augmented with fire. Then we get to the last leaf—the last 2,000 years. On the first side of the last leaf is the first Christmas, and the reverse side brings you up to now. You must read far down on the last page before you get to the industrial revolution. In the last bit of the second column is the industrial revolution. The last six or seven lines of that last page's last column encompass everybody in this room.

In this sentence or two, you find man suddenly very enamoured of his technology; the last two or three lines record what man has done in the last 20 to 40 years, in which brief part of his existence he has used up more resources than all the rest of the life story told in all the volumes around the room—he outdid all living things in just those last few lines. The final line or two represent the period since World War II, when man started broadcasting about the land the kinds of poisons Rachel Carson was so worried about.

The whole series of miracles each of us is—each living thing is—is the product of the slow, slow course the life force has run through without a break, in the volumes representing all the flow of time since life began. We need to be extremely careful in those last few lines of time, about what we are inflicting upon that life force. One of the first things we're going to run short of is the variety, the magnificent complexity, of living forms that surround us. We seem compelled to eliminate them faster than we can learn what they mean or how much we may need them. As our society itself gets more complex, we oversimplify them.

There is not much more to say right now. I wish there were a chance to argue with our four speakers so I could make sort of a discussion of it. Maybe you will.

I didn't find anything I could disagree with at all on what any of them said, except that I might challenge Dr. Day with having understated what the population growth means. In this doubling of the population within 45 years that is constantly predicted, it doesn't mean putting the expansion over in the Mojave Desert; it means someone sharing your seat, in effect, someone waiting in a telephone booth with you, waiting for the long distance operator to say, "I'm sorry, sir, circuits are busy." It means one person more where every person is right now. Imagine this in everything you do every day, and you'll become a little bit more motivated about preventing it.

One other thing I might disagree with is some of the mention of food surplus in the prepared statements. One of the things that might help us is to decide that we will no longer tolerate the self-fulfilling prediction: the one that says, "In 40 years from now there are going to be X million people in the Bay Area, and there are going to be X million people running across the Sierra, and therefore we must build new roads." Such predictions always tend to fulfill themselves.

If I could give only one slogan it would be a paraphrase of what you see on the bumper strips, where the skiers say, "Let's stamp out summer." I would say, "Let's stamp out the self-fulfilling prediction." When somebody says to you, "Fifty years from now there are going to be 80 million people in California," just say, "Oh, no, there won't be." Take it upon yourself to do something about it.

MODERATOR GILLIGAN: I have been impressed by a statement made some 35 years ago by a philosopher of the time, James Truslow Adams, in an article in *Harper's Magazine,* entitled "Diminishing Returns in Modern Life." He said, "Because 20 people can enjoy a beauty spot, it does not follow that 2,000 can. If we go beyond a certain concentration of numbers in use of the land—instead of giving everybody everything—nobody has anything. This law is hostile to much of democratic doctrine and man's aspirations, but has nothing to do with their existence or power."

This prospect is now approaching crushing reality, as our speakers have made clear, and a number of questions to our speakers reveal this concern. The first question is for Dr. Leopold: "Do the current accelerated efforts for outdoor recreation planning by Federal, state, and local governments, with their new funds and broad authorizations, present threats to wilderness?"

DR. LEOPOLD: It seems to me that the problem of recreational development is that there is not a clear enough distinction drawn between the separate kinds of recreation, some of which are dealing with mass recreation, a perfectly logical, natural, and human interest, but a separate kind of recreation, which does not improve in its return to the individual in proportion to the numbers of recreationists.

All recreational planning at the present time, it seems to me, is directed toward improvement of mass recreational facilities, and it should—in my view—be balanced by an equal effort to preserve recreational potential not utilized en masse.

MODERATOR GILLIGAN: Dr. Condliffe, "What are the economic consequences to America in terms of gross national product and prosperity when we successfully stop the population growth?"

DR. CONDLIFFE: I was born too late or too soon to worry too much about the gross national product. This is a calculation in monetary terms of the value of all goods and services produced in the country. In some ways it is a fictitious calculation. If you own your own house, you get an imputed value for the rent that you don't pay. If you want to get this number up, the quickest way to do it would be for everybody living under community property law to pay his wife half of his income as salary. Then it would be included in the gross national product. You should not be mesmerized by a number which must constantly increase. The gross national product per head is something else. I'm not quite sure that we have to increase aggregate G.N.P. all the time, but it is always in relation to the population that you should consider it.

MODERATOR GILLIGAN: Maybe you would handle this one, too, Dr. Condliffe: "Do you think we should progress, as we call it, or should we slow down and demand less in order to stretch our resources for more?"

DR. CONDLIFFE: I think the best answer I can give to that is that I was on the subway in New York with a Japanese visitor and a very efficient American friend, on my first visit to the United States. Somewhere along the line our American friend ran to another train that was just coming in on the other side of the track, and the Japanese visitor asked, "Were we on the wrong train?" My efficient friend said, "No, but we were on a local train and this is an express we are on now. We will save three minutes in getting to Columbia." When we got out on the Columbia Station on 116th Street, the Japanese said to him, "What shall we do now with the three minutes that we have just saved?"

MODERATOR GILLIGAN : I would like to ask Will Siri to read a question which I have given to him and asked him to answer.

MR. SIRI : This question says: "What specific action should we take to solve the problems of saving wilderness? For example, should laws be passed with penalties limiting the number of children? That no more freeways be built on scenic lanes? And, finally, we do so damned much talking, but we don't do anything about it."

This is the kind of question that we hear occasionally, and I'm delighted to have an opportunity to answer it, even if it is only in two minutes. I don't think the person who wrote this question reads the conservation literature too carefully, or looks about him to see exactly what is being done. In the past ten years we have made more progress in establishing the whole concept of wilderness than has been made in all the previous past.

There are now young professionals entering the field. In the last year alone some 14 pieces of legislation were passed by Congress, two of them major legislation, acts that were passed and signed by the President. We are making excellent progress. We are making progress as fast as we could ever hope to do it in this tempestuous world. There is every sign of progress; it is in the growth of attitudes across the country.

And don't forget one other thing—there are four, five, or six hundred of us sitting here today. There were in the last meeting, and there will be in future meetings. There are present the heads of Federal and state agencies who are listening. I don't think you can assume for a moment that these men are not listening carefully to the voices they hear about them. They are subject to the same pressures that everyone else is, and they are hearing the voices of the conservationists and the demands for wilderness across the country. We also have the gentlemen and ladies of the press who will be—hopefully—carrying a bit of this message through their various media.

These are signs of definite action. This kind of thing cannot be done overnight. There is no single law that we can pass that will suddenly preserve for all time the whole wilderness we want. There are too many conflicts, too many social, political, and economic forces. You cannot legislate as of today the limitation of families. This can come only with a change in attitudes across the country—when a majority of our citizens agree to such a law. Our purpose here today is not to try to push through Congress a law that limits families—not in 1965.

Our first and most important function as the Sierra Club, as the Wilderness Conference, is to educate the people to the dangers that confront us in an overwhelming population, and ultimately the people themselves enact such legislation.

We will never accomplish this without talking. This is our principle mode of communication. Talking is essential, and if one becomes anxious or apprehensive that it is all talk and no action, I can only suggest that you look about you, make an assessment of what has been achieved in the last year, and then in the preceding years.

We are making progress. We are making very good progress. Don't forget that last year saw the establishment of the idea of conservation and of Beautiful America injected into our national policy in the form of the State of the Union Message by the President.

There is every sign that we will preserve more wilderness, and I'm absolutely certain, too, that as the years pass more lands that have been used for production in the past will be restored to their original state. I am not at all pessimistic about the future and I don't believe we have talked enough. We not only need to talk to ourselves, we need to talk to everybody in the country.

MODERATOR GILLIGAN: It is interesting to remind ourselves that in the seven or eight years it took to pass the Wilderness Bill even in its present form, Congressmen have informed the Sierra Club that at various periods they received more mail on this question, largely favoring the passage of the Wilderness Act, than they did on any other single issue. This was during the period of consideration of it, so it is doubtful if the bill might have been passed if public response had not been apparent.

DR. DAY, "What has been the basic cause of population arrests in those countries where growth has tapered off—for example, Hungary, Italy, and so on? Have they not reached a physical limit in their environment rather than a realization of the dangers to come?"

DR. DAY: No, far from it. Actually, they are living better today than they have ever lived before—in a material sense, at any rate. Their death rates are lower than ever before, and the way they have done this and brought about this cessation of population growth is by means of control over fertility.

When you ask about causation, there are many factors involved. I can tell you what the techniques are. The technique in Hungary, unfortunately I think, is primarily abortion. About two abortions, legal abortions, occur for every live birth. Abortion is also widespread in

Austria, France, Belgium, and it is widespread in this country also. Here it is illegal; it is illegal in France, too, but abortion is a very important technique used in those countries.

Contraception is another. Coitus interruptus is a very widespread technique and has been used for 150 to 200 years as the prime technique in France. But the point I wanted to emphasize is that these people are not at the limit of the productive power of their land; they are living at a far higher level in this regard than ever before.

MODERATOR GILLIGAN: Here's another question: "Has any thought been given to the economic encouragement of a substantial tax reduction for families with two children or less? What effect would this have on population control?"

DR. DAY: I think the main effect it would have, definitely a secondary effect, is to put the government behind the idea of small families. Otherwise, I see no particular advantage. All it does is to distribute families by means of the market mechanism. People who are rich, people who can afford to have more children, as they so nicely tell us, are people who will perhaps not object to paying an additional tax.

What you are doing with this proposal, if this were enacted, is to tax people on the basis of their children. I am concerned with children; this is the reason I am in favor of the cessation of the population growth; this is the reason we have limited our family. We are concerned with children, and I think the important thing is to have an equitable system of taxation. I don't think this sort of system would be equitable. It would be the equivalent of distributing childbearing according to the market mechanism; if you have the dough you can have the kids; otherwise you can't. I can't see that.

MODERATOR GILLIGAN: Before we let you go, I would like to ask you one more question:

"How would you control the population increase in California, which is not necessarily a birth increase but an increase caused by immigration from other states? How does a popular state like California defend itself from being over-run?"

DR. DAY: I don't know, really—unless you could change your climate. The best thing to do perhaps is to discourage the expansion of industry. People are not going to go where there are not any jobs. Get rid of the defense industries and get rid of the war effort. Another way, of course, is to cover it with concrete.

DR. CONDLIFFE: I would like to say I don't think discouraging the defense industries would work. What makes Dr. Day think that the man who is going to be unemployed wouldn't sooner be unemployed in California?

MODERATOR GILLIGAN: Speaking of concrete, I have a freeway question for Dave Brower: "What about the freeway threat to the parks in California and ultimately the use of the automobile as the major form of transportation?"

MR. BROWER: The freeway threat to America's parks, national and state, or to areas that are of park caliber, of course, is still a very great one. I am thinking of the Redwood state parks, the potential Redwood National Park, of a national reservation of some kind we ought to have along the Big Sur Coast, some of the finest coast anywhere. I am concerned about Yosemite and Sequoia, where major highway improvements are contemplated still.

The threat is a serious one. I wish Nat Owings were here to field this question. He testified on this before the State Natural Resources Committee and tried to put the automobile in perspective. He did it very well, and I can't in two minutes. He reviewed very quickly the history of this country. We began, you might say, on our canal kick in the early days. We then moved to railroads; they would cope with everything. We then looked to the automobile, and we are on that kick right now. But it is not going to last. It can't. We can't continue to put as much productive land, scenery, and housing under pavement as we are now doing. We have to find another solution.

We have been talking about mass transportation; we are moving toward it slowly. If you watch the papers, we are moving toward it too slowly. We can't afford to have every man require a ton of steel to drive himself from his bed to his desk, and 300 square feet of concrete to park it on at either end. We can't keep doing this.

We do have an enormous amount of inertia in our planning that makes us think that paving is the only way to solve the problem. It isn't. The longer we put off the problem of moving toward mass transportation, the less economically feasible it is. It is not good economics and it is not good land use to keep on paving and paving. Somehow we have to stop being slaves to the automobile.

We have a thousand teaching jobs, for example, in our schools that are unfilled because we don't have the teachers. We don't pay them enough. We spend six times as much on automobiles as we do on education. I don't think that is a very good posture for this country to assume. Once we get over that kick, the concrete will diminish.

MODERATOR GILLIGAN: Dr. Leopold, "Is the building of tunnels to divert water from one watershed to another in the best interest of any watershed?"

DR. LEOPOLD: I think it is incorrect to try to take one specific measure and point at that and say, "Let's get rid of that." Rather than say that it is not useful to divert water from one basin to another, let's look at this in quite a different way.

As I said earlier, if the public is informed concerning what is involved, what objectives are to be achieved, and what these different alternatives might mean to society, the public is going to choose in the long run. The difficulty at the present time is that the public does *not* know what is involved, and therefore they have to concentrate on this measure or that measure, such as "We are against transmountain diversion," or "We are against dams," or whatever it might happen to be, because they are not informed. They are looking at too small an aspect.

I am making a distinction here between education, which everybody says is a great thing, and informing the public for the purpose of helping them determine the effects of the various alternatives.

MODERATOR GILLIGAN: Dr. Condliffe, "Why don't we have more economists directing their attention to parks and preservation and other conservation problems?"

DR. CONDLIFFE: I suppose most economists have to work for their living. Many of them have worked for conservation on their own time. But to do the detailed studies that are necessary, requires a good deal of time and somebody has to pay for this. When Mr. Brower comes to S.R.I., I hope he realizes that we are not very cheap to employ.

I had a comment on the last question. There are occasions when a tunnel to transfer water from one side of the mountain to the other can be very useful and very productive. Such a case is in the mountains of Australia where they trapped a little river in the snow fields —which ran down every spring and devastated the farms in its short course into the sea—and put the water into another river and had a supply of water for the inland farms. I don't see how anybody was done any harm by this; certainly a great number of people have considerable benefit. But each case has to be studied on its own merits.

MODERATOR GILLIGAN: Dr. Leopold, "In the interest of getting water to arid areas in California for food production, do conservationists deplore completion of the Central Valley Water Project?"

DR. LEOPOLD: This is exactly the same thing I was saying before, and I agree with Dr. Condliffe completely. It is all a question of the local situation, what the local people want—not necessarily local in the sense of a given community, but what the community of the general society of an area wishes.

The engineering plans that have been developed for any part of the country have a certain reasonableness. What I am objecting to is that whether it be any California plan or any other plan in the United States, generally the public is not informed about the alternatives involved, and therefore they tend to limit their view to a particular aspect without understanding all the things concerned.

I maintain that if the engineering planners gave the people a better idea of what really is involved and what are the alternatives—they are going to be hard choices and are not going to satisfy everybody—the choices finally made would tend to be better for society as a whole.

MODERATOR GILLIGAN: Mr. Siri, "What will be the political effects of population limitation, assuming a world political structure such as the present one in the future?"

MR. SIRI: In the course of completing the keynote address this morning, I inadvertently dropped the crystal ball, and the answer to this one seems a little dim. I don't think the political effects will be particularly different from what they are now in the world of the future. We have been discussing wilderness and what man does with his own living space. We have not been discussing what man does to man. If there is to be a profound change in this, I'm afraid somebody's going to have to invent a better man. I don't think anything we do with our environment or our world will particularly alter the variety of views or conflict of views or our determination to implement our views in whatever way we choose.

If, in effect, you are asking whether reduction in population in the future will reduce the risks of war, I doubt it.

DR. CONDLIFFE: I would like to tell you the nightmare story of the invasion of China by Soviet Russia. On the first day the Russian armies penetrated 50 miles and took a million prisoners. On the second day they penetrated 100 miles and took 5 million prisoners. On the third day they got a telegram from Mao Tse-tung, "Give up now?"

One of the implications of the question was that if we limited the population and other people didn't limit theirs that we would lose our position in the world. This I don't believe.

II

LUNCHEON
April 2, 1965

Introduction

CHAUNCEY D. LEAKE

The Spirit of the Place

ALBERT E. BURKE

INTRODUCTION

≫ *Chauncey D. Leake*

Ladies and gentlemen, I have recently had the pleasure of hearing our distinguished speaker. He has a lot of interest and enthusiasm and brilliance.

Albert Burke received his college training at the University of California at Los Angeles and his Ph.D. in International Relations on the international aspects of resource use from the University of Pennsylvania. He held the post of Director of Graduate Studies in Conservation and Research Use at Yale University from 1951 to 1957.

Dr. Burke is a former director of the American Institute of Resource Economics and a former consultant in industrial development for the Connecticut Light & Power Company on natural resources and conservation.

He and his wife have spent considerable time working and living with the American Indians on reservations in the southwestern part of the United States, and I am delighted to know there is good understanding here for those great people. His travels have taken him all over this country, and he has spent several years in Europe, in Soviet Russia, and in the Far East. He is an authority in the field of conservation as well as in the fields of geography, geopolitics, and world affairs.

In 1957, Dr. Burke was appointed Educational Television Consultant for the National Broadcasting Company where he produced the award-winning series entitled "Survival." His programs were challenging, provocative, and it was indicated they filled a vital need. He had quite an article in *Look Magazine,* where he was called an "Angry American." I don't think he is angry at all. He has a lot of good, joyous, peaceful comments to make to us. Dr. Burke.

[77

THE SPIRIT OF THE PLACE

➽ Albert E. Burke

The topic I will discuss with you today is not an easy or a happy one. It involves the difficult job of communicating with people—in terms of the subject of this meeting, communicating information not always palatable to many people.

I do not say this because many people are against such things as wilderness areas. Rather, they really know very little about them. Whatever one says about wilderness of any kind in our time shakes their view of things as they are, as they know them. It suggests what they know may not necessarily be so.

Because, there is a problem involved. In order to set it in proper perspective, let me tell you a story. I heard it during my last tour of Naval Reserve duty. Occasionally I pick up a story that way which can be repeated in public. This story concerned three waves up for promotion. Whether or not they were promoted would depend upon how well they knew their naval rules and regulations and could use them to solve a problem. They were informed by their examining officer, a Commander:

"Your problem happens on the day you decide to spend part of your leave time rowboating on the bay. About the time you reach the middle of the bay, a troopship comes by, loaded with several thousand young men who have been away for several years, during which time they have seen no one even remotely resembling you three in that boat. As the troop ship comes closer, you note that several of the men on that ship start to lower a motor launch. And that is your problem. How would you deal with the matter?"

The Commander turned first to the brunette for her answer. She replied that she would put the oars on that boat to maximum use, to get to shore before the men in the launch caught up with them. At which point the Commander interrupted—irritated—to point out it was obvious the launch would overtake the rowboat long before it reached the shore.

He then turned to the next, a redhead, for her response, and she said, "Sir, I would do as she suggested. I would get those oars going to reach the shore, but when they caught up with us, I would use those oars to let them know this would be no easy thing."

The Commander considered that, then turned to the blonde and asked for her answer. The blonde looked at the Commander, with a puzzled frown, then said, "But, Commander, what is the problem?"

The problem began with the first fellow off the Mayflower—I do not at the moment recall his name. By the time he had taken his first few steps into the New World, an arrow whizzed by his ear and hit a tree close by. When he turned to see who had shot the arrow, he could not see the man, because that Indian was hiding behind a tree. From that early incident to this time, Americans have had it in for trees.

The point is, whether or not this version of history is true, there is an attitude amongst Americans to explain how we feel about things, what we think about things. That attitude has much to do with the ease with which we have cut down trees from coast to coast. It is the attitude you can see gleaming in the eye of the bulldozer operator who is about to clear land anywhere in this country for a housing project. If there is a single tree in 50 acres of land, it will be his primary target. And, not facetiously, this attitude toward trees is most important to understand if we are to do anything at all to convince the public at large there is something valuable in wilderness areas— something worth saving. This was, interestingly, the first topic in a series of programs done for NBC, when I was with that organization eight years ago. It has much to do with this topic I have been asked to discuss here. It is the heart of the problem of communicating ideas that may not be palatable to the public at large.

In that series of programs for NBC, I wanted to explain why it was that Americans were able to do so much with *things,* that so few other peoples had done, or were able to do. To do this, I discussed the matter with a Catholic priest, a Protestant minister, and a Jewish rabbi. I had an idea I wanted to test in my conversation with those men, an idea that had occurred to me during the years I had spent out of this country while a student. That idea was that one of the most important things we did not understand about ourselves was that we do have clear, direct roots into our religious past. We are part of a historical process that includes our Judeo-Christian background.

In order to do that particular series of programs for NBC, I went into that Judeo-Christian theological background, as far back as the Book of Genesis. There, one of the verses most of us take very much for granted—certainly would not deny—seemed to me to be an appropriate first step in explaining the matter of attitude about things: why we have done things to the land—and to things on it, in it, and above it—that so many peoples around this planet have not done. That first step was Verse 26, which states that man was created in the image of God—which shocks few amongst us, though it is still a somewhat novel idea to several hundred millions of people around us. Verse 26 also states, more pertinently to this topic, that this special creation in God's image also has special rights: specifically, that man was granted dominion over the things of the earth that creep, crawl, fly, etc.

I put this information into a television script for the series of programs and precipitated a major crisis. It was submitted for approval to the office of Continuity and Acceptance—a network euphemism for censorship—and it was rejected. It was too touchy a topic. It might displease people with religious bias. It would be better not to air the concept.

I would like to be able to tell you that the man who voiced that objection and enforced his judgment was improper in his conduct and did not know what he was talking about, that there was, in fact, no reason for doing this. I cannot do that. You see, I have been in my kind of television for 15 years. I can assure you that in that time I have learned that the people who disapprove of things are the writers, while the approvers rarely show the same initiative— particularly if there happens to be a degree or two after their names. That elite amongst the population finds it difficult to stoop to the level of writing to any network about any program. The result is on your air waves this minute.

There is a price to be paid for saying things on the air that irritate others. One price I paid several years ago involved the wilderness areas we are concerned about here. It concerns the story I told last night about a series of programs I presented on the American Indian. It was stressed that the Indians had, and have, a very close relationship with their land. It was made clear that it is not possible to understand the American Indian in our history unless one understands that relationship. The words "Mother Earth" used in our history come from the Indian "Earth Mother." It is an indigenous expression, very much involved in the way the Indian lives and thinks to this day. The conflict we have had with the American Indian has been, from the beginning, a difference of opinion about how land should be used. As Verse 26 implies, we Judeo-Christians see land as a commodity. It can be bought, sold, given away. We have dominion over it. The Indian does not agree.

In that series of programs I told the story of a friend who is a research scientist. He had been involved in a project called "Bionics" study. His was a study of insects and how they operate, in an effort to produce a mechanical method to duplicate their abilities. He had been given a particularly difficult assignment, as his part in that study. He was to search for a way to improve a radar system, by finding a way to select and then lock the system on the true targets and not the decoys accompanying future missiles or weapons directed against the United States.

It was a difficult assignment. He worked at it until he was close to collapse. He was instructed by his doctor to take time off and rest. This he did by going to the Wilderness Area in the Bitterroot Valley in Montana. One day, while fishing, he noticed the movement of a praying mantid on a nearby branch. It was a fairly windy day with dust and flying particles of many kinds in the air. Yet that praying mantid seemed able to select quickly the true target he was waiting for, while ignoring similar-sized and shaped particles around it. It occurred to that vacationing scientist—who was in that Wilderness Area to re-create himself—that the mantid was doing the very thing he had been trying to accomplish. He went back to his laboratory, and from the praying mantid developed the improved radar system required.

I told that story and I said, "Obviously there is a need for a natural laboratory where such things are still possible. In this case, while re-creating himself, while enjoying the recreational possibilities of that Wilderness Area, that man saw the answer to problems bearing on the survival of the United States." It was a dramatic story, deliberately oriented to the man in the street. Wilderness areas have many valuable qualities, but unless those qualities are stressed which can capture the interest and imagination of the man in the street, you cannot stir him.

The response to that program made clear that the problem and the possibility of survival through that place did reach the layman. It also reached three of my sponsors, who immediately cancelled the program. In Boise, Idaho, it was not wise to speak favorably about the Wilderness Bill. The depositors in the bank sponsoring the program there made their income by feeding animals in grasslands and by cutting down trees. When I suggested some areas should not be touched for any purpose—even for earning income—that was interpreted as more than slightly subversive of their private interests. Actually, I had done nothing of the kind. But it resulted in the loss of sponsors. Because the problem was, and is, to communicate ideas not necessarily palatable to the general public. This is a problem that has a solution, bearing on an area of education most of us in academics talk about continually. The general public is barely aware of it *as* a problem. It has direct ties to this problem of preserving natural areas.

Several years ago, I was asked to participate in a conference in Connecticut where an effort was to be made to do something close to the hearts of most academicians. That was to find a better way to turn out the well-rounded student. I hope to meet this object of the academic heart's desire one day. I have met many students who could be rolled in almost any direction, because they had no direction, but I have met few really well-rounded products of our institutions of higher learning.

One of the main reasons we do not have such products is that an imbalance exists in their training, as has often been stated. But the imbalance is not where it is currently fashionable to say it is. We are turning too much of our effort to the sciences, I am told, not enough to counter-balancing work in the humanities, social sciences, etc. It is an interesting point of view. I am familiar with the statistics frequently quoted by modern Panglossians to show that this week there was an increase over last week of 17 percent in the number of students going into engineering; 28 percent more are going into medicine this year than last year. Rarely, however, do such statistics include the facts about dropouts after six weeks of classes, because fields like engineering and medicine require more of its members than stout hearts and good intentions. They require basic information and training. How many students, in the same periods reporting increases in science-oriented young people, have gone into mathematics courses? To understand the sciences, tool subjects like mathematics are essential. Rarely is there an increase in the enrollment in those courses to match the expression of good intention by students headed for the sciences.

This conference was called to redress that imbalance. It was the hope of those attending that the need for tool courses would be recognized. Further, that it would be made clear no American could be prepared to act intelligently, vote intelligently, or think intelligently about the problems affecting the future of the nation unless he or she understood how much of our lives is affected by what science and technology do.

There was a problem involved in this particular meeting. It had been called for 3:30 PM, and I had a 2:00 PM class. Those of you who know the geography of that part of New England know that it is not possible to leave New Haven when a class is over at 3:00 PM and still get to Hartford in one half hour. But I tried. And as I came flying low through one of the underpasses on the Merritt Parkway heading for the meeting, I noticed a car parked off the road, on the green. My foot hit the brake pedal as I attempted a gradual slowdown, but not for the reason you may have in mind. It was not a police car parked there, waiting for someone like me to come along.

I must tell you at this point that when I was taught by my father to drive the family car out west, it was impressed upon me that one never passed anyone who seemed to be in trouble on the road. There were not many cars on those roads. It was the thing to do. In this instance, the car by the side of the road had an open hood. Standing by the hood was a very lovely young 18 or 19 year old from one of the local women's colleges. It was late April, I recall, and it gets quite warm in Connecticut by that time. That lovely young thing was dressed to accommodate the weather. Mother nature had been extremely kind in providing her with all the right accommodations, but it was because my father had made very clear to me as a young man that one always stopped to help others in trouble, that I did so.

Unfortunately, the story does not go beyond that. I called the Automobile Club when it was clear little could be done by an amateur, but I carried away with me the idea for the cartoon which hangs over my desk to this day. It shows a much perplexed young lady standing by a stranded car, with the title "The American Dilemma." That young lady was about to graduate from an American institution of higher learning in 1956 with a vague awareness of something wrong with that technological product of twentieth century science, but with little understanding. That kind of understanding is a tool subject for Americans who would understand the value in our time of wilderness areas. Only a small part of this land remains in that state of being. Yet about the time our science and technology has reached the point where we can understand the need to look into the working of things as they are in nature—between such things as praying mantids and radar systems, and agriculture and microclimatic controls—that young lady, not trained properly to know the ties between science and her world, is about to complete her preparation to live in that world.

To do anything about problems like those in preserving wilderness areas, we must turn out well-balanced young people. This is the most basic of educational problems in every American community. Without this background, people can be convinced that such things as multi-purpose dams, as Dr. Leopold discussed them this morning, are possible. They cannot analyze, as he did, the meaning of that word. They can be pushed into costly and useless projects that can do more harm than good. We need well-balanced curriculum in our schools to turn out the necessary well-rounded student.

In this connection, I should like to comment about educational television and the classroom, as discussed during your last conference, and compare this to the methods I have used in commercial television. With several exceptions this year, my programs have not been on educational channels. I have preferred this because too much of what passes as educational television has a stilted, academic approach that leaves the man in the street unmoved. The simplest truth is that few academicians know how to talk to the man in the street. Too many are protected in their fields by unintelligible jargon.

Television puts ideas before the public under far different conditions than involve a captive audience in a classroom. When your ideas are displayed to a public, stimulated and edified by a talking horse moments before your appearance and further informed after your appearance by one of those cockeyed versions of American history out west called "adult westerns," be assured you must speak a language that can be understood or your viewers exercise their privilege to shut you off. They are, you see, a free people. Free to be ignorant as they please. That is *as* important an aspect of freedom as their freedom to be knowledgeable. Too much of what appears on educational television is on far too remote a plane to reach most people.

In the field of communications it is much more difficult to speak to that man on the street than it is to speak to your own colleagues. Academicians, by and large, are too busy wording their ideas in the manner best designed to protect them from the criticism of their colleagues to devote the effort required to reach the people. The tragedy in this is that their intelligence is thereby lost to the nation. And there is a desperate need for their knowledge.

In 1956, Dr. Leopold and I attended a conference concerned about man's role in changing the face of the earth. On that occasion, at one point, someone raised a question that has remained with me since: "What is the responsibility of the scientifically trained person beyond producing his own ideas? Should he be concerned that his ideas may fall into the hands of someone who may do with them precisely what the scientist hoped to avoid?" It seems to me the burden of that responsibility—to see to it that an idea is not misused or abused—rests with the men who produced the ideas, with the men of knowledge. There is no time left for intellectual or academic snobbery amongst our men of knowledge. They can speak clearly to the public to be understood, as they had better do in this matter of our wilderness areas.

I have tried to discuss this matter with PTA groups, service clubs, women's organizations, and management seminars, to mention a few. Articulating ideas, simply, is not enough. There is another problem to overcome, a problem of semantics. What is a "natural area"? Most Americans today live in urban places. Most of our friends and neighbors would not know a natural area if they fell over it in broad daylight. When they are in a natural area, as we have discovered when taking our urbanized friends into such places, we find not only a lack of understanding about its value, but fear as well.

We camped out one night with friends from Teaneck, New Jersey, in a forest area of the Southwest. They slept in sleeping bags for the first time in their lives, or tried to—not quite hiding their fear of all manner of poisonous insects and dangerous animals. A noisy cricket was an object of alarm. They understood nothing about the area. How does one reach such people with any argument about saving natural areas? What are we talking about? Who articulates these ideas and reaches such people? Whose responsibility is it to do so?

One of our problems in this connection is that our men of knowledge have no dialogue with the pillars of the American community. I have in mind, by the use of that term, those men who have invited me on occasion to lunches or dinners at their city clubs, golf clubs, university clubs, and the rest. There, in conversation with many such "pillars," I have listened to some of the worst, unmitigated ignorance about the political, social, economic, philosophical, and religious aspects of our affairs. This is more than casually unfortunate, because the bulk of authority in this society is in the hands of economic men. Where authority is, responsibility lies—or should in our nation. But does it? I remember one such conversation in the Duquesne Club of Pittsburgh, where casual conversation at lunch became policy on the national level, because a United States Senator at that luncheon was informed by his hosts about their feelings and desires in relation to things political, social, economic, etc. But what those men discussed, they understood poorly. In today's America, where the layman feels increasingly powerless to deal with the nation's problems, power is concentrated in the hands of economic men. Their ignorance is dangerous because it is expressed in what they do with advertising budgets in supporting talking horses dealing with inanities, instead of supporting talking men dealing with issues—like the wilderness areas. Men of knowledge must get to these men of power. Together, they are the keys to the nation's future. They are the few who can do more to help you get what you want in this matter of wilderness areas than all the men in the street.

All I have tried to say here is in line with a very old American tradition. Through the record of the earliest writings of the men who made this nation, there is a consistent theme: a concern about what came after them, about posterity. They were most concerned about what would happen if they did not look ahead to plan for posterity. Their plan was laid out generally in our basic papers, and underscored in the words which said that they had banded together in nationhood to—among other things—promote the general welfare. Self-interest was not to be this nation's major interest. We would do well to know and remember this in our time. But most of all, we would do well to think for ourselves about these matters and not be pressured by others to think as others do, because it is easier and safer that way.

There is an even older tradition than the one just mentioned. About 2,200 years ago, a young Greek, who was quite concerned about this matter of communications and responsibility, was worried that the people of that day were not living up to their traditions. The most important of those was the tradition that the people could rule themselves. One of the more important prerequisites for self-rule is that people think for themselves, adequately and properly, about all the things that have to be thought about to make the idea of self-rule work. The Greeks of his day were not thinking for themselves, because they did not have to. Whatever their problem, they could take it to the oracle in the temple nearby, request assistance or the answer to their problem, and it was done. The dependence of those Greeks on the oracle was destroying their ability to think for themselves. It was easier and safer to let the oracle do it.

That young Greek knew he would have to find some way to shake his people's belief in the infallibility of the oracle, if he were to show them the need to think for themselves again. But how does one discredit an oracle? He thought about it long and hard. Finally, one day, he decided he had the answer. It would consist of a series of questions not even an oracle could answer. The questions would involve a hummingbird which he would hold in his hand while saying to the oracle, "Oh, all powerful, all wise, all knowing, all great one, what do I have in my hand?" The young Greek expected the oracle to tell him, "Young man, you have a hummingbird in your hand." At which point he would say, "That is true, all wise, all knowing, all powerful and great one; but tell me, is the bird alive or is it dead?" Now, if the oracle told the young man that the bird was alive, he would squeeze his hand to kill the bird, then open his hand to show the oracle that the bird was dead. If the oracle replied that the bird was dead, he would open his hand, the bird would fly away, and, in either case, the oracle would not have answered the question correctly. This would destroy the idea that the oracle was infallible, that an oracle could be trusted in all things.

Off to the temple went that young Greek, with the bird in hand. "Oh, all great, all knowing, all wise and powerful one, tell me, what do I have in my hand?" asked the young man.

"You have a hummingbird in your hand," was the reply.

"That is true, all wise, all great, all powerful, all knowing one; but tell me, is the bird alive or is it dead?"

The oracle's answer was, "Young man, the answer to that is in your hands."

As indeed, ladies and gentlemen, the answer to all we have discussed this day is in your hands.

III

THE IMPACT OF TECHNOLOGY

The Conservation of Energy in Its Various Forms
JAMES BONNER

The Plot to Drown Alaska
PAUL BROOKS

Problems of Pollution
JAMES K. CARR
with
A. J. HAAGEN-SMIT

T. ERIC REYNOLDS, *Chairman*

THE CONSERVATION OF ENERGY
IN ITS VARIOUS FORMS

>>> *James Bonner*

The usual approach to the problem of energy conservation is a matter of projecting how long our supply of coal or petroleum or water power will last and then trying to forecast what is in store for us when these natural energy resources are gone. But it is clear today that neither hydroelectric power nor power derived from conventional fossil fuels can satisfy the energy requirements of our rapidly expanding economy. That nuclear energy can and will fill the need is equally clear. There is, therefore, no logical basis for the thesis that rivers must be dammed to supply power to a power-requiring society. The preservation of a river as a thing of beauty, rather than as a dam site, hastens but infinitesimally the time when all power will be derived from nuclear energy. In terms of the subject of this conference, therefore, I foresee changes taking place over the next few generations which will make it possible to insure our having both adequate energy resources and wilderness with us for a long future.

This is true despite the fact that our culture in the United States will continue to become more complex for many years. It will demand and consume an ever-increasing amount of material resources; hence the pressure on these resources will continue to grow.

A primary problem is that people have an apparently limitless capability to consume objects. Even if we were to decree that each of us could not purchase any more objects—automobiles, television sets, electric toothbrushes, etc.—to decree that everyone is to have the same number of such artifacts as he owns today, our culture would nonetheless continue to become more complex. This would happen because as our high grade resources are exhausted, we go to lower grade ones. Today we make iron out of lower-grade ores than those used a few years ago. We get petroleum from oil wells that are 5 miles deep instead of 500 feet deep as they were a few years ago. To get a constant amount per year of any given material requires a continuous expansion of our technological industrial complex. Just to stay where we are, we must continuously make a bigger industrial plant.

Moreover, our industrial civilization is spreading over the entire face of the earth. It is the avowed intention of the leaders of all of the underdeveloped nations to bring to their countries the benefits of industrial civilization. We can project from what is going on today and what has gone on in the recent past how fast industrialization will spread. These projections suggest that, for example, India in a hundred years will be about as industrialized as Japan is today. In the meantime Japan will have become enormously more complex. As our industrial culture gets more complicated in the United States and spreads to all other nations, and as the human population of the earth continues to increase, we can readily understand that the demand upon material resources will in the future become enormously large, even by American standards today.

Within a few generations the high grade resources of minerals, metals, power, water, and lumber will all have been exhausted, and we will have to make use of the very low grades of natural resources. It is therefore a comforting thought to know that all of the metals that we need for our industrial civilization—iron, aluminum, copper, zinc, tin, etc.—are contained in the common rocks of the earth's crust. They are not there in very high proportions to be sure, but they are there, nonetheless. If we scrape up some granite and grind it up, we can get the iron and the aluminum and the tin and the copper, and indeed all of the metals that are needed to make all of the metal objects we need. The time will inevitably come when we will have to go to this rock-grinding kind of industrial activity.

The power needed to accomplish this, however, would be considerable. To put this in perspective, there is a handy number which we should know and remember. For each one of us in the United States there is in use today approximately ten tons of steel—steel in all of its various forms—buildings, rails of railroads, automobiles, refrigerators, and so on. To power this steel—to move it around so that it can do things—takes each year an amount of energy equivalent to that contained in ten tons of coal. This is true for all of the nations of the earth's surface. And as the level of our industrial civilization increases and the amount of steel rises year by year, so also does our consumption of energy, the energy which each of us consumes in the form of electric power, gasoline, heat, etc. It is quite clear, then, that over the next few generations the consumption of energy in the United States will increase by several fold. As industrialization spreads, the consumption of energy by the people of the earth will increase during the next four generations by at least twenty fold. The amounts of energy which will be essential to the maintenance of our world-wide industrial culture will exhaust the world's petroleum reserves in very short order. At a meeting such as the present one, a hundred years from today, the conferees may perhaps reminisce about the days when there used to be such a thing as petroleum. Petroleum will, by then, be but a dim memory in the minds of most people. We will continue for some time to extract energy for our culture from coal, but here again there is but a finite amount of coal under the earth's crust. It will slowly be mined out; and at a rate of energy consumption twenty-fold that of the world today, even coal will not last very long.

It is fortunate that just in the nick of time we have found new ways to get energy to power our industrial machine. We have learned to use atomic energy. Indeed electrical power from nuclear power plants is now very nearly competitive in price with that from plants fueled by conventional fossil fuels. Economic projections suggest that by the year 2000, two-thirds of the energy consumed in Western Europe will issue from nuclear power plants. These projections also suggest that the last old-fashioned coal power plant will be built about 1980.

In a forecast of the future distribution of energy generation among the various sources of fuel, my colleagues and I have come to the conclusion that one hundred years from today, something like 90 percent of all energy consumed in the world will be generated by nuclear power plants. Only nuclear power can supply the required amounts.

For how long can we depend upon power generated by nuclear power plants? The uranium and the thorium required for nuclear reactors are, like coal and oil, fossil fuels. Uranium and thorium were made once, namely when the elements were made during the creation of the earth 5 billion years ago, and they are not being made today. How much uranium and thorium is there on earth? How long can they power our industrial machine? There is not very much energy available in the deposits of uranium and thorium that are considered economic to mine today, but as time goes on and the requirements for these elements continue to increase, we will mine lower and lower grade deposits. We must recognize, then, that the time will inevitably come when we will obtain our uranium and thorium from the common rocks of the earth's crust. How about that? They are there, too! We take some granite and we grind it up, and we extract uranium and thorium and use it to fuel an atomic power plant. Enough energy is produced to pay for the energy cost of mining and grinding up the granite, to pay for its processing, and there is, in addition, an enormous amount of energy left over. This energy will be used, of course, one hundred years from today, in part to accomplish the extraction of the other needed minerals from the granite which we have ground up. The remainder will be used to power the energy-consuming network of our industrial civilization as a whole.

I foresee, then, that in the future, as high grade deposits of minerals are used up, the mining industry as such will disappear, and that to take its place, we will develop vast, all-purpose chemical plants. These will be situated on the beach and will grind up and process the common rocks of the earth's crust. Each plant will contain within itself a nuclear power plant, which will generate energy for the United States power network. Each plant will produce all of the mineral resources which we require. Each plant will also include within itself a vast water recovery plant, for purification of ocean water, because by the time of which we are speaking, the waters which run down the rivers of our land will no longer suffice for our industrial requirements. We will have to use water reclaimed from the ocean on a vast scale. And finally, I am happy to report that even if all of the people of the earth were to be supported by such vast all-purpose plants, and even if the population rises to a level of 6 to 9 billion people, two to three times the present level, and even if all of them live on a standard appreciably higher than that of the United States today, we will nonetheless mine down through the common rocks of the earth's crust at a rate of only a few millimeters a year. There is enough material in the common rocks of the earth's crust to power our culture for literally millions of years to come.

In our projection of the energy requirements of the United States and of the world over the next few generations, it is clear that hydroelectric power plants can at best provide a vanishingly small proportion of the total. For example, at the level which we have just discussed, 6 to 9 billion people, all living at a level of power consumption somewhat greater than that of the United States today, water power fully developed over the whole earth's surface could supply less than 4 percent. Thus as time goes on and as our culture becomes increasingly complex, the power available to us from hydroelectric sources will become an ever increasingly insignificant proportion of the total. There is just not enough water running down the rivers of the world to supply any significant proportion of the world's total power requirements.

Let us then consider the future of our technological culture as it bears upon the preservation of our natural heritage, our wilderness. It is often said by industrialists that we must use this or that particular resource because our economy demands it, that the particular resource is required for the welfare of our people, that it is necessary that we grind up this mountain, or build that dam, in order to provide material resources for the people of our nation. Such a statement is not, in fact, true. If we deny the request and do not build the dam or do not allow exploitation of the mountain, all that we thereby do is to speed up very slightly in time the moment which must inevitably come in any case—the time at which we will inevitably mine the common rocks of the earth's crust.

Seen in historic perspective, the perspective of a thousand years from today, the result of not building some particular dam today or of not digging up some particular mountain will be merely that we have hastened very slightly the time which must arrive in any case—the time of arrival of the "New Stone Age."

I think this is a heartening prospect. It gives us a logical, rigorous basis on which to base a conservation movement, a sound philosophical basis upon which we can logically base requests that a particular wilderness area be preserved. Such a wilderness area is not required as a natural resource, no matter what it contains, because in the long run the amount of the resource which it contains will become infinitesimally small as compared to our requirements and as compared to what we can and will obtain from other sources. If we, for example, do not build a particular dam today, we do not rob our people of any of the energy which they will require in future; we will merely speed up very slightly the time at which essentially all of our power will be derived from nuclear power plants.

What then can we do to use this philosophy to help us in the preservation of wilderness areas? I think there are two things that we can and should do. The first is to use every mode of communication to make known this philosophy to all of the people of our nation and indeed of the world. We must successfully transmit to everyone the message that it is sensible to preserve a wilderness, even if it contains a resource, because that resource isn't really unique and is not required. We can supplant it with our new technology—which is, in any case, what is going to happen. This, then, is the first thing we must do. We must try to get our message across.

The second thing we can do, and something I think we really must do, is to try to find more positive reasons upon which we can base arguments about how wilderness areas are good for people. For example, instead of saying in a qualitative way that wilderness areas are beautiful and that they are good for us, I think we ought to consider ways in which we can quantify and better identify the benefit and its exact nature. We should be able to state how much benefit is obtained per capita from a wilderness area. I think that this identification and quantification of the values of wilderness areas need not be necessarily based in immediate economic terms. We could, if we put our minds to it, think of other kinds of benefits, not directly economic, but nonetheless measurable and identifiable. We might try to find evidence that relates use of our wilderness areas to health benefits. Perhaps, for example, every person who visits a wilderness area lives longer, or is less likely to be a juvenile delinquent. Perhaps people who visit wilderness areas have more creative thoughts than people who do not do so. Creativity is fashionable in the United States today. Let us find ways to link the existence of wilderness areas to things that are positive goals for Americans.

I think that if we rise to the challenge of these two tasks—that of communicating to the people of our nation that there is a real alternative to the exploitation of wilderness areas and that of finding good, sound, positive reasons for their preservation—and if we are effective in our task, we can look forward with rising assurance to the preservation of wilderness in our country and in our world for literally hundreds of generations to come.

Yukon River near Rampart Village, Alaska

Wildlife Country: The Yukon's Ramparts

PHOTOGRAPHS BY PHILIP HYDE

THE YUKON RIVER is best known as the gold-miners' route to the Klondike. Its place in Alaskan history suggests that of the Ohio, Mississippi, and Missouri river systems in the opening of the West. But now the biggest, most expensive dam ever has been proposed for the Yukon River; such a dam would create the largest artificial lake in the world. Many Americans—including Alaskans—are questioning whether this is the best use of our natural resources.

"... we drew alongside another cow moose swimming the river,
and marveled at her power and speed as she fought her way across the current,
the water parting at her straining neck and shoulders
and bubbling whitely over her barely exposed withers.
This is prime moose country."

Brooks' party
on the Yukon River

Yukon Flats

To conservationists, one of the most valuable parts of the entire river is the area known as the Yukon Flats, which extends approximately from the town of Circle downstream 300 miles to Rampart Canyon, north-west of Fairbanks. More than 100 miles wide, this vast network of shallow water sloughs, marshes, and potholes, with its grasses, cattails, and aquatic vegetation, provides one of the finest wildfowl breeding grounds in North America. There are an estimated 36,000 lakes and ponds on the Flats.

From the air, the Flats appear as a giant abstract painting with muted colors and swirling shapes. Wherever there is a current, teardrop sand-bars grow into islands, tinted here and there with green as the willows take hold. Bends cut off by the ever-shifting river are left as oxbows of stillwater.

The Corps of Engineers' plan—a single great dam at the narrows—would put the entire Yukon Flats under several hundred feet of water and create a lake with a surface area greater than Lake Erie.

Sunset in Lower Rampart Canyon

"This is wild count

d its values are wilderness values."

Native family of Venetie, Alaska. The village council of Venetie, where few Indians are on relief, voted unanimously against the Rampart Dam project.

The native people are Athabaskan Indian, not Eskimo. Seven of their villages on the Flats would be drowned if the dam is built; some 1200 natives would need to be evacuated. The livelihood of many more would be affected.

Some 270,000 salmon pass the dam site annually on the way to spawn in the upper waters of the main river and its tributaries; this fishery above the dam—important to all of Alaska and particularly important to the Indians—would be eliminated and the product of the entire system greatly reduced.

Fish wheel below Fort Yukon

*"If every river has its voice, the voice of the Yukon is the rhythmic groan
and plosh of these giant wheels turning slowly in the current,
their webbed baskets now and then scooping a silvery fish
from the thousands pouring downstream.
Nowhere in the world do salmon ascend rivers for such distances
as they do in the Yukon system."*

*Salmon drying
at Stevens Village*

Rampart dam site

A sense of now or never hangs over the Rampart project. "I feel that if it is not built now," said the mayor of Anchorage, "it probably will not be built." Claims for the project are not modest. One of its strongest supporters, a group called Yukon Power for America, believes that—in addition to injecting a billion dollars into Alaska's sagging economy— the dam will provide electricity at three mills per kilowatt hour and thus attract industry, notably aluminum, to Alaska. Many economists and businessmen disagree.

But the impact on wildlife resources is definite. A yearly production of 1½ million ducks, 12,500 geese, 10,000 cranes, plus many moose and small fur-bearing mammals would be completely lost. Although, as Paul Brooks points out, to question a billion-dollar handout may be almost immoral, virtually every national conservation organization has gone on record against the Rampart Dam project. For as the official report of the U.S. Fish and Wildlife Service to the Corps of Engineers states flatly: "Nowhere in the history of water development in North America have the fish and wildlife losses anticipated to result from a single project been so overwhelming."

Text adapted from statement by Paul Brooks.

THE PLOT TO DROWN ALASKA*

≫ *Paul Brooks*

As any small boy knows, the presence of running water is a compelling reason to build a dam. Most boys when they grow up turn to other things, but a select few go on to join the U.S. Army Corps of Engineers. Here, under the heading of flood control, navigation, or power production, they build dams beyond the wildest dreams of youth. Some of these dams are necessary and some are not; all of them provide jobs for the Engineers. Most of them involve huge expenditures of Federal money. The biggest, most expensive of all is now on the drawing board. Damming the mighty Yukon River at the Ramparts in east central Alaska could create the largest artificial lake in the world.

To the layman, the name Army Engineers, as the Corps is usually known, suggests activities concerned with the military. This is logical but inaccurate. The Army Engineers, consisting of the elite of West Point (originally established as an engineering school), have a superb military record, but most of their work has nothing to do with war. They are the most independent executive division of our government. Engaged largely with "improvement" of navigable rivers and harbors, they have access to the biggest chunks of pork in the barrel, and they are beloved by Congress. They have, on occasion, successfully defied the President. Yet in all their glorious history they have never had a chance quite like this to show what they can do.

Here, in brief, is the plan. A glance at the map will show its magnitude. The Yukon River, which rises in the Yukon Territory of northwest Canada, crosses 1,300 miles of Alaska from east to west, flowing northwest from the Canadian border to touch the Arctic Circle at the

---

*This talk was subsequently published in the May, 1965, issue of the *Atlantic Monthly*, and condensed in the August, 1965, *Reader's Digest*. Copyright, 1965, *The Atlantic Monthly*.

town of Fort Yukon, thence west and south to empty at last into the Bering Sea.

Best known as the gold-miners' route to the Klondike, its place in Alaskan history suggests that of the Ohio, Mississippi, and Missouri river systems in the opening of the West. Now, alas, the great stern-wheelers, reminiscent of Mark Twain's days on the Mississippi, lie rotting on the riverbank at Whitehorse, wood-hungry engine stilled, proud pilothouse a nest for swallows. But in a changing world, where leisure gives more time for recreation, where a burgeoning population needs room to breathe, the Yukon has taken on a new importance. To conservationists, the most valuable part of the entire river is the area known as the Yukon Flats, which extend approximately from the town of Circle, now reached by an extension of the Alaska Highway, downstream 300 miles to Rampart Canyon, northwest of Fairbanks. More than 100 miles wide, this vast network of sloughs and marshes and potholes provides, in addition to its fur-bearing population, one of the finest wildfowl breeding grounds in North America.

To the Corps of Engineers, this presents a golden opportunity. By building a single great dam at the narrows, they could put the entire Yukon Flats under several hundred feet of water. They would thus create a lake with a surface area greater than Lake Erie or the state of New Jersey. The lake would take approximately twenty years to fill. The dam, 530 feet high and 4,700 feet long, would cost, at lowest estimates, one and a third billion dollars. The money would come from the Federal Government. Though more than a million dollars has been spent in preliminary engineering surveys, the principal flow of money will start when and if the dam is voted by Congress.

The sales campaign behind Rampart is a promoter's dream. Starting out with a $100,000 budget, which will probably soon be doubled, an organization called Yukon Power for America has been formed for the sole purpose of pushing Rampart through Congress. YPA includes businessmen, newspaper publishers, chambers of commerce, the mayors of the principal cities in the State. There is even a junior membership for schoolchildren at 25¢ a head.

YPA's first publication is a colorful brochure entitled "The Rampart Story." The claims are not modest. The basic one is, of course, cheap electrical power. By providing electricity at three mills per kilowatt hour, the dam will, according to YPA, attract industry—notably the aluminum industry—to Alaska.

Furthermore, "once lured to Alaska by Rampart's mass of low cost energy, several industries would find new uses for the State's coal and gas reserves." The reservoir itself "will open vast areas to mineral and timber development," and provide unlimited recreational potential. Sixty million dollars a year would be spent on construction alone, and "new workers with their families would more than double the population." In planning this paradise YPA has widespread support beyond that of the Engineers, who first launched the project. The Golden Valley Electrical Association is solidly behind it. An organization called North of the Range terms Rampart "Alaska's future. . . . We have to come forward with both guns blazing."

A sense of now or never hangs over the battlefield. "We are going to have to do a tremendous selling job," said the mayor of Fairbanks. The mayor of Anchorage agreed: "The political climate is favorable now for the project. I feel that if it is not built now, it probably will not be built." Congress, as one YPA official put it, feels "an obligation to the new State."

Senator Ernest Gruening was equally frank in addressing the State Legislature at Juneau. "Alaska is confronted with the task of catching up after years of Federal neglect. We were excluded from the Federal aid highway program, and virtually excluded from Federal aid power projects." It is also a matter of catching up with Russia, where he had seen "hydroelectric power dams larger than the largest in America."

The Senator's administrative assistant, George Sundborg, author of a book on Grand Coulee Dam entitled *Hail Columbia,* not only reflects this urgency but glories in the speed with which things are moving. "The sun shines bright on it." Grand Coulee, he recalled, required years of study. "And here we are practically ready to start the dirt flying on Rampart."

Simultaneously he castigated the Interior Department's Fish and Wildlife Service for speaking against Rampart "without waiting for the evidence to come in." "To be realistic," Sandborg said, "what can we expect of a Department whose Secretary seems to conceive of his mission as dealing primarily, if not exclusively, with parks and recreation"—and who was off climbing Mount Kilimanjaro when he should have been pushing for Rampart in the McKinley Park Hotel? Representative Ralph Rivers went further. The time has come to have "a heart to heart talk" with Udall. "I should think that Stewart has a few punches coming, and I can see that we have adequate talent on the [Alaska] delegation to administer those punches."

When an army takes the field under such dynamic leadership, questions of fact are roadblocks to be swept aside. It is good for morale to simplify the issue: "Are you for ducks or for people?" and to sneer at the opposition: "Do we," said Mr. Sundborg, "—please excuse the metaphor—have all our ducks in a row . . . ? Far from it. Rampart has its enemies—waiting with a loaded shotgun and a red-hot mimeograph machine."

Employing a novel criterion for assessment of land values, Mr. Sundborg dismissed the entire area to be drowned by the dam as worthless: it contains "not more than ten flush toilets." After exploring the region for over a week by small boat and by plane, I challenge this estimate; the figures are grossly exaggerated. The Yukon Flats are wholly without plumbing. This is wild country, and its values are wilderness values. To get a fair impression of it, one must visit not only the Flats themselves but the river from the Canadian border down to Tanana, since the Army Engineers' long-range plan includes two dams in addition to Rampart, one of which would back up the water as far as Dawson in the Klondike.

A small group of us made this trip in the summer of 1964, launching our two flat-bottomed, scowlike "Yukon River boats"—twenty feet long with outboard motors—at Eagle and finishing ten days and 650 miles later at Tanana, the first town below the Rampart Dam site. At Fort Yukon, halfway on our journey, we hired a small plane and for five hours flew low over the Flats and surrrounding territory, north to Arctic Village and west as far as Rampart Canyon.

Eagle, where our trip started, was the first incorporated town on the Yukon. The Army base, with a garrison of 2,000 at the turn of the century, had the responsibility of keeping law and order along the river. Still standing are the huge stables for the Army mules. Nearby, lining the riverbank, is an Indian village; the native people are Athabaskan Indian, not Eskimo. The river here is already broad, swift, and brown with silt, bordered by alluvial flats or steep cliffs of limestone and shale. Camping the first night opposite a dramatically beautiful bluff, we could hear the current swishing past its base with the rush of a brook in spate.

Next morning, as the early mist began to burn away, we let the motors sleep and drifted. The only sound was the hiss of silt against the boat, like the finest rain on an attic roof. Near the mouth of a tributary, whose clear blue waters met the muddy Yukon in a sharp line, a cow moose stood placidly with a yearling bull at her side.

Flocks of mallards congregated near the shore, and somewhere from a slough echoed the cries of red-throated loons. Though in August we were too late for the nesting season, we saw more and more waterfowl as we approached the Flats: pairs of widgeon, small flocks of white-fronted geese, and two sandhill cranes, long necks outstretched and wings beating slowly as they flew directly overhead.

Later on, when we had reluctantly started the motor, we drew alongside another cow moose swimming the river, and marveled at her power and speed as she fought her way across the current, the water parting at her straining neck and shoulders and bubbling whitely over her barely exposed withers. This is prime moose country.

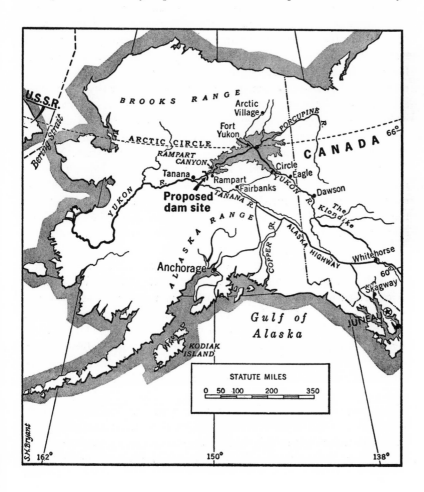

We counted ten the first day on the river, including several old bulls with that great spread of antlers which makes the Alaska moose one of the most impressive creatures in the world. America's largest land animal, it is the chief source of meat for the native peoples in many parts of the state. This is wolf country, too. These much maligned animals, so necessary to the balance of nature in the Arctic, have not yet been exterminated along the Yukon, as they have over so much of their former range. In the mud at the water's edge their round tracks, like those of huge dogs, mingled with the print of the moose's sharp hooves—though only once did we get a glimpse of this living symbol of the wilderness.

Above the Flats, signs of human habitation were few. An occasional trapper's cabin, a channel marker from the steamboat days, an Indian family's summer encampment, where salmon were being caught in fish wheels, dried on racks in the sun, and smoked in rough frame shelters like tobacco sheds as winter food for men and dogs. If every river has its voice, the voice of the Yukon is the rhythmic groan and plosh of these giant wheels turning slowly in the current, their webbed baskets now and then scooping a silvery fish from the thousands pouring upstream. Nowhere in the world do salmon ascend rivers for such distances as they do in the Yukon system. Now in August, over a thousand miles from the sea, the king salmon had already gone by, but the silver-salmon run was at its height, and dog salmon were yet to come. Visiting with an Indian family, we sampled the "squaw candy" made from choice, delicately smoked strips of king salmon, which fetch a high price at Fairbanks and points south.

At the town of Circle the character of the river changes. Here the Flats begin. The main stream becomes diffused in a maze of secondary channels, sloughs, eddies, shallows, and dead ends, which once or twice baffled even our native Indian boatman. It moves as swiftly as elsewhere, but is broken by ripples and torn by snags and sawyers (one always thinks of Mark Twain) rhythmically rising and falling in the current. The hills have been left behind; the table-like bog stretches to the horizon (not very distant when your eye is just above the water), relieved occasionally by an isolated bluff, such as the one where we met an archaeologist and his staff from the University of Alaska, who were unearthing traces of an ancient Indian settlement. They shared the site with a pair of peregrine falcons, aristocrats of hawks from the days of chivalry. As we climbed up to watch and photograph one of the two young—still tufted with white down but learning to fly—the falcon circled and shrieked overhead, while her mate, the tiercel, perched restlessly nearby. The peregrine falcon has virtually ceased to breed in the Eastern states, owing in part to the sterilizing effect of pesticides. The few birds we see in the East are raised, like these, in the Arctic. For how long?

From the peregrines' eyrie we could look far out over the Flats, as the early men who lived there must have done to spot their game. But to read this vast landscape, one must, like the peregrine, fly over it. Our opportunity came at Fort Yukon, whose airstrip, since the decline of river traffic, is its connection with the outside world. All day we flew in a single-engine plane, adding a third dimension to our surface view of the past few days. The first impression was that of a giant abstract painting with muted colors and swirling shapes. Actually it is a picture in imperceptibly slow motion. Wherever there is a current, teardrop sandbars are growing into islands, tinted here and there with green as the willows take hold. Bends cut off by the ever-shifting river are left as oxbows of still water. The key to the more distant past—to earlier and long-abandoned riverbeds—is the pattern of vegetation. Since spruce grows best on the higher, better-drained ground of the natural levees built along its edge by the river itself, one can trace the course of successive channels by the concentric curves of spruce forest. There are ponds of every size and shape, deep blue in contrast to the coffee-colored river, bordered with bright green sedge. So clear was their water that, flying low, we could make out moose tracks crisscrossing the mud of the bottom.

There are an estimated 36,000 lakes and ponds on the Yukon Flats, the area which, if Rampart Dam is built, will become one huge wind-swept lake. This abundance of *shallow* water, of grasses and cattails and aquatic vegetation, makes ideal breeding ground for waterfowl. Such country is vanishing fast, both in the United States and Canada. Despite agricultural surpluses, we continue to drain our marshes to make more farmland. Wheat farms and settlements are relentlessly encroaching on the famous pothole country of Canada's Prairie Provinces, where the great bulk of our waterfowl now breed. In the light of these facts, are the Yukon Flats, which contribute as many ducks as the entire "lower forty-eight" states, worth saving? Shift the camera back to Fairbanks, Anchorage, and Washington, D.C.

"Search the whole world," continues Mr. Sundborg (following his vain search for flush toilets), "and it would be difficult to find an equivalent area with so little to be lost through flooding." Rampart's supporters are impatient with what they call "the old, old arguments of professional conservationists"—as if truth somehow decayed with age. Others brush off "this duck business" with wisecracks such as "Did you ever see a duck drown?" Anyway, if the ducks don't like it, they are smart enough to go elsewhere. Just where is not specified; other breeding areas are already being used to capacity. (Senator Gruening, who surely knows the geography of the state he represents, makes the remarkable statement that the ducks "can nest all over the other 98% of Alaska.") Some birds that breed on the Flats migrate to Siberia; are we, asks an officer of YPA, going "to mollify these feathered defectors"? Officially, YPA takes the matter more seriously, but offers reassurance: "Despite some early fears of wildlife and fish displacement in the reservoir area, available evidence shows no significant effects." This statement is so outrageously untrue that one must in charity call it a supreme example of the public relations man's power of wishful thinking.

The official report on the Rampart project by the U.S. Fish and Wildlife Service to the Corps of Engineers states flatly: "Nowhere in the history of water development in North America have the fish and wildlife losses anticipated to result from a single project been so overwhelming." A nesting habitat which contributes annually about 1,500,-000 ducks, 12,500 geese, and 10,000 little brown cranes to the four North American flyways would be completely destroyed. The resultant lake would provide no substitute. "The fluctuating reservoir would have steep, wave-washed shorelines which would preclude formation of marshes suitable for nesting or shallow waters productive of waterfowl foods. The large expanse of open water would provide no nesting habitat."

What of the salmon run? At least 270,000 salmon pass the dam site annually on the way to spawn in the upper waters of the main river and its tributaries. If Rampart is built, fisheries upstream will be totally destroyed and, with the loss of the upstream spawning grounds, the product of the entire system drastically reduced. Fish ladders for such dams have been proved impractical, and fantastic schemes for trapping the salmon and transporting them upstream in barges not only would be prohibitively expensive but would not work anyway, since the fry would never find their way downstream through several hundred miles of dead water.

What about other wildlife? The moose range, with an estimated eventual carrying capacity of 12,000 animals, would of course disappear. So would martins, wolverines, weasels, lynx, muskrat, mink, beaver, otter, which taken together represent an annual harvest of some 40,000 pelts, or about 7 percent of the entire Alaska fur production—a sizable item to write off in any state's economy, which is, nevertheless, far below the future potential. The report concludes: "We strongly oppose authorization of the Rampart Canyon Dam and Reservoir project."

Last, but certainly not least, what of the people who live along the river? Seven villages in the Flats would be drowned; some 1,200 natives would be evacuated; the livelihood of 5,000 to 6,000 more in Alaska, and an estimated 3,500 in the Yukon Territory, would be affected by the reduction of the salmon run. After a quick flying trip to the area, Senator Gruening reported that most of the natives he talked to were in favor of the project. My impression was somewhat different. I did find two articulate supporters of Rampart: one, an elderly native resident of Fort Yukon, thought that the building of the dam would provide jobs for his numerous sons; the other, a white trader at Rampart Village, felt sure that he could get a whopping price from the government for his establishment and retire in luxury. But this did not, I think, represent the majority view. I detected a reluctance on the part of these people to having their homeland obliterated, to being located elsewhere with no means of livelihood, to spending the rest of their lives on relief. To be sure, there was a feeling of fatalism: if the government wants the dam, they will build it—what can we do?

I wonder whether the Senator may have confused this resignation with consent. He is certainly aware that at a meeting of village leaders in Fort Yukon they expressed themselves against the Rampart project. Did he, I wonder, visit the village of Venetie, an independent self-respecting community north of Fort Yukon which, unlike the latter, has very few people on relief. Here the village council voted unanimously against the project. Perhaps they did not agree with the Senator that they live in "an area as worthless from the standpoint of human habitation as any that can be found on earth." It may be expedient to displace these native people and drown their towns for the greater good of the State as a whole. But let's not pretend that they like it.

Below the dam the effects could also be disastrous. At present, the seasonal flooding of the river replenishes the marshy shores and pothole lakes, which in turn support the furbearers, the moose, the waterfowl, and the fish on which the Indians depend. Their whole way of life may be destroyed if the dam is built. Rampart's backers speak confidently of the jobs that will be created by this vast construction project. But no technical training program has been established for the native people. Who will get the jobs, untrained Indians or construction workers brought in from the "lower forty-eight"?

The sun may be "shining bright on Rampart," but many areas are still in shadow. There has not been time for adequate study; all one can say for sure is that the losses, tangible and intangible, will be immense. Will the gains justify the cost? What in fact is the true source of support for this glorious new project of the Army Engineers?

The ostensible purpose is hydroelectric power: power in huge quantity at low rates. Not, in this case, to meet a demand that already exists. Alaska needs power, but it neither needs nor can use it on any such scale as Rampart would provide. The approach has been from the opposite direction. Unlike Grand Coulee Dam on the Columbia River, where contracts for the use of the electricity preceded construction, Rampart is a speculative venture. If the dam is built, can the power be sold?

A number of economic studies have been commissioned to provide the answer. Three of them are particularly illuminating. In 1961, the Battelle Memorial Institute made a twenty-year projection of Alaska's development. It found that "tourism offers the most promise for immediate and continuing returns to Alaska." Major mineral developments are conjectural. As for power production, "future energy-use in Alaska will be characterized by increasingly keen competition among hydro, coal, gas, and oil, and possibly nuclear in the farther future."

In January, 1962, Arthur D. Little, Incorporated, of Cambridge, Massachusetts, delivered its report to the State of Alaska. It examined the industrial possibilities of petroleum, natural gas, coal, and electric power. To Rampart's boosters the report came as a shock. "Regarding the larger hydroelectric projects, it should be noted that it is not correct to speak without qualification of low-cost hydroelectric power. Low-cost for any particular project must be accompanied by high-volume use. The larger hydroelectric projects proposed for Alaska as capable of providing 2 or 3 mill power would . . . produce a quantity of power many times the ability of present Alaskan industry, commerce and population to absorb."

Rampart is a 5 million kilowatt project. "At its present stage of de-

velopment even a tie-in with all smaller industrial, commercial, and
domestic power markets would not fully utilize a hydroelectric project
with an excess of 1 million kilowatt capacity unless several electric-
intensive industries appeared on the scene within a short period of
time. This is, of course, a possibility but not a very realistic expectation."

This was not the sort of talk that the politicians and the Army Engineers wanted to hear. What to do? As quietly as possible the report
was filed away, though news of it did leak out. Meanwhile, the Army
Engineers had proved equal to the crisis. Realizing in advance that
the A.D.L. study was not going the way they wanted, the Engineers,
in consultation with Rampart's promoters, commissioned another report, from the Development and Resources Corporation of New
York, to deal specifically with the market for Rampart power. No
time was wasted: the new report was issued within a year—only
three months after the other—and printed by the U.S. Government
Printing Office. Its conclusions were much more satisfactory. "Based
upon the marketability of Rampart power and the benefits resulting
from its use, as indicated by our analysis, our study affirmatively suggests: A decision to move ahead soon with the Rampart project will
prove nationally prudent, wise, and desirable." This was more like it.
The D. and R. report was given the widest possible distribution and
instantly became the Bible of the Let's Build Rampart Now movement—though critics have suggested that it reads more like the
prospectus for a bond issue.

Both studies were, of course, preliminaries. In February, 1965, the
"field report" of the Department of the Interior, which has jurisdic-
tion over the project, was released. Though it avoids final judgments, the facts set forth must be cold comfort to the promoters and
the Army Engineers. Clearly the importance of mineral deposits in
Alaska has been seriously exaggerated. The thesis that low-cost
power will necessarily lead to resources development is not valid. The
timber industry will not benefit; on the contrary, over one billion
board feet—three years of Alaska's current timber production—will
be destroyed.

Several alternative sources of waterpower would cause far less
damage than Rampart: Wood Canyon on the Copper River, the
Yukon-Taiya project near Skagway, and, most immediately practical
of all, Devil's Canyon on the upper Susitna River between Fairbanks
and Anchorage. The latter project was officially approved by the De-

partment of the Interior in 1961. It would provide more than adequate power for Alaska's immediate needs, while causing virtually no damage to its wildlife or other natural resources. As an alternative to Rampart, Devil's Canyon has the strong support of Alaska's conservationists.

Most significant in the long view is the prospect of cheap nuclear power, which may make Rampart obsolete before it is built. Progress here has been very rapid during the past two years. General Electric estimates that orders for atomic power plants will be 60 percent higher in 1965 than in 1964, representing 10 percent of all new generating capacity ordered this year. The president of the Aluminum Company of America recently announced that the aluminum industry has eliminated its dependence on hydroelectric power, that he favored steam power for new plants, and that the next Alcoa plant would be built in the Ohio Valley.

With labor rates among the highest in the world, with the heavy costs of transportation over such great distances, with a lack of local mineral resources to be exploited, central Alaska does not in fact offer an irresistible lure to the aluminum or any other industry. What if the dam is built and the lure fails to work? In that event, say Rampart's rooters with a certain note of desperation, we'll ship the power south to where it's wanted, ignoring the fact that this would require the passage of high-power lines across Canadian territory. Since British Columbia takes the view that it has enormous power potential in its own province, much closer to American markets, the chances of any such arrangement are dim indeed. Canada's Minister of Northern Affairs and National Resources, Arthur Laing, has made clear his country's opposition to such power lines. "We do not think that undertaking is desirable on all the known facts," he says of the Rampart plan.

Alaska would in any case lose most of the long-term benefits. And at the present time, as the Bonneville Power Authority points out, there is already a surplus of power in the Pacific Northwest.

Rampart will provide hydropower in abundance. What else? Water storage and irrigation are the last things this area needs. Primitive values would of course be wholly destroyed. This leaves only recreation among what they call the multiple uses. "The Rampart Story" makes a big thing of the recreational potential of the 280-mile-long lake that will be created: "Fresh water boating and sailing . . . hunting lodges and fish camps on scenic shorelines . . . marinas, dock and float plane facilities—all accessible by rail, highway, and air."

Let's see. The lake will be on the Arctic Circle, at the same latitude as Great Bear Lake. At a guess the ice will break up in early July. High winds and waves on a body of water this size require seagoing vessels. The lake will be filled with dislodged timber, the shores strewn with debris. Since the country is almost flat, the drawdown at the dam site could create a mile of mud flat between the "marina" and your boat. Hardly the perfect recreation area.

So, finally, we come to the immediate motive behind Rampart Dam. The achievement of statehood has brought problems to Alaska. Taxes have gone up, and there are relatively few sources to tap. For the past twenty years, the building and manning of military installations, including the famous DEW Line, have channeled vast amounts of Federal money into the area. Now the defense boom has tapered off. Gold mining and the salmon fishery have both been on the downgrade. Though large sums have been spent seeking oil, not enough production has been obtained to take up the slack. Thus, at the very moment of transition between territory and state, Alaska is facing a down-sliding economy. Employment needs a shot in the arm. If the dam is built, the amount of Federal money spent on construction in the five years preceding initial power production will, according to the D. and R. report, exceed the total amount spent for military construction in Alaska from 1950 to 1955. The whole job will pour a minimum of one and a third billion dollars into Alaska and probably a great deal more. As one legislator is said to have remarked privately, Rampart Dam will have served its purpose if it is blown up the day it is finished.

Recognition of Rampart as a sort of colossal make-work project—a Federal subsidy for the state economy—explains a great deal, but it puts the conservationist in a curious position. He becomes the enemy of prosperity. To question a billion-dollar handout is almost immoral. Virtually every national conservation organization has gone on record against the project. But to think of it as a contest between cash and conservation is unreal. This is not an either-or choice, least of all in Alaska. As both biologists and economists have pointed out, Alaska's fish and wildlife resources are, by the very nature of the country, the backbone of its economy, the principal source of its cash income. Closely related is the growing tourist trade: visitors who come not just for the hunting and fishing but for the refreshment of space and true wilderness in an overcrowded world. In terms of the needs of the nation as a whole, Alaska's wilderness is a priceless resource. Orderly development of its waterpower will not necessarily destroy it. Spectacular but speculative ventures like Rampart will surely do so.

Prominent citizens are to be found on both sides of the controversy; beneath all the shouting lie honest differences of opinion. The very magnitude of the project brings home the terrible responsibility that goes with the possession of limitless technical means for controlling nature. If the dam is built and turns out to be a colossal blunder, ten million cubic feet of concrete cannot conveniently be blown up and swept under the rug. Before the dirt begins to fly, we have to face the unavoidable question: how far does a financial speculation like Rampart Dam justify us in permanently changing the face of the earth?

PROBLEMS OF POLLUTION

⋙ James K. Carr

I couldn't help but think, hearing Mr. Brooks, that it was a little difficult for me, a professional engineer who spent some 15 years in the dam building business, to come here before this group.

Fortunately, I worked for the Bureau of Reclamation and not the Army Engineers. After I left the Bureau, I was with the House Interior Committee as a staff assistant for a few years, and I recall one time at a hearing that a man came up to the late Senator Engle, then Congressman and Chairman of the Sub-Committee, and said, "Isn't that Carr the fellow that was with the Reclamation Bureau?"

Senator Engle said, "Yes."

The man said, "He's not working for your committee, is he?"

And Senator Engle again said, "Yes." The Senator looked at him for a few seconds and added, "Don't worry, Carr is a Reclamation Bureau refugee who is going through the congressional delousing vat." So I hasten to tell you that even though I am a professional civil engineer and have been involved in a number of dam construction projects, I have been through the Udall delousing vats and you need have no concern.

I was asked to speak on the problems of pollution in two areas, in the wilderness and at your front door; and I remember the letter from Wallace Stegner to Secretary Udall, which said:

"Something will have gone out of us as a people if we ever let the remaining wilderness be destroyed . . . if we pollute the last clean air and dirty the last clean streams and push our paved roads through the last of the silence, so that never again will Americans be free in their own country from the noise, the exhausts, the stinks of human and automotive waste."

He was pleading to prevent an America in which we would be ". . . committed wholly, without chance for even momentary reflection and rest, to a headlong drive into our technological termite-life . . ."

I think you will agree that America the Beautiful dies a little each time mountain meadows are littered, crystal clear streams are polluted, and the alpine stillness is shattered by the sounds of blaring radios, motor scooters, chain saws, and portable electric generators.

You and I are here—in this Biennial Wilderness Conference—to help arrest and to stop, if possible, this erosion of the unspoiled and natural world. You make this effort, and I do too, because we are concerned with the basic values which are affected by man's relation to the land.

Responding to your request to speak on "Problems of Pollution," I wish to speak of pollution in the broad sense, and I want to emphasize these three points:

. . . a successful drive to save the remaining wilderness from devastation will depend largely upon the force of the expanding effort to preserve the natural beauty of America in all its aspects.

. . . public pressure which threatens to pollute and change the wilderness by incompatible forms of use will be reduced in proportion to the increase of substitute, diversified recreation areas which can siphon off that pressure.

. . . preventing pollution of the far-off wilderness will be successful in proportion to the degree we can abate defoulment of the air, reduce noise, and improve the cleanliness of water in the streams, lakes, and bays which are virtually at our front door—in proportion to how much people care about the total environment in their daily lives.

In short, your problems of preserving the wilderness are part of the greater problems—providing more opportunities for healthy, wholesome outdoor recreation and preservation of beauty in the total natural environment. The achievement of your objectives will depend upon how successfully you help muster the momentum of a National Conservation Crusade.

When I speak of conservation I prefer to define it as did President Kennedy in his March 1961 message to the Congress. He said: "We must reaffirm our dedication to the sound practices of conservation which can be defined as the wise use of our natural environment; it is, in the final analysis, the highest form of thrift—the prevention of waste and despoilment while preserving, improving, and renewing the quality and usefulness of all our resources."

Eric Sevareid drew a little sharper focus on wilderness when he cautioned that, "Progress has to be defined to mean preserving and cherishing as well as changing and improving."

The problems of pollution therefore—whether in the High Sierra or on the shores of the city—are problems of waste disposal.

I emphasize that success in saving the wilderness depends largely on the force of the expanding effort to preserve the natural beauty of America. My remarks are not intended to depreciate the already outstanding achievements of this group or minimize in any way the strength of your dedication. Rather, I want to point out that there are relatively few people in this country who have had the opportunity and the privilege to know what you are talking about. The great majority, even in this city, are completely engrossed in the daily struggle for existence. Their needs must take the time of government leaders at all levels and drain off the energies and the funds which could otherwise be used to acquire the disappearing dunes and other uncrowded areas.

When Secretary Udall began the battle for more national seashore parks, only 240 miles of the 3,700 miles of the great sweep of shoreline from Campobello to Corpus Christi were dedicated to public use. Excessive crowding is the natural result. The surge of 200,000 people to New York's Jones Beach on a summer day demonstrates the shortage of space near metropolitan areas. And we should not forget that except for metropolitan New York, San Francisco is the most densely populated city in the United States.

Meeting metropolitan man's needs by preserving unsullied areas in remote places is a recognition that man has a soul as well as a body.

If we are to prevent despoilment and waste, preserve and cherish nature's gifts, renew the quality and usefulness of the nation's natural resources, then we need to awaken the people and through their government to get on with the job.

But make no mistake—government officials alone cannot do the job. This new Conservation Crusade will succeed only if we are all in it together—public agencies and private enterprise—government representatives, local, state, and Federal.

The second point I make—saving the beauty of the wilderness by providing alternative recreation areas—is a necessary, positive approach. Decrying the flood of people into wilderness areas and national parks won't keep them untarnished. Certainly Yosemite Valley today would shock John Muir. Noise, traffic jams, air pollution, litter, threats to water quality, police, inconsiderate neighbors, and other effects of too many people in one place make the seekers of breathing space "feel at home" in the worst sense of the word. Let's face it. We need more camping and picnicking facilities in some of the hundreds of other beautiful places which are within reach of the metropolitan millions. If these substitute areas are not provided and advertised, the existing parks will resemble the nightmarish, noisy world that Wallace Stegner referred to.

Right now in California, we have a chance to provide more recreation areas and reduce the pressure on existing parks and wilderness. We can do it by supporting a bill introduced by Congressman Harold T. (Bizz) Johnson, to establish the 250,000-acre Whiskeytown-Shasta-Trinity National Recreation Area around the lakes created in Shasta and Trinity Counties.

If approved by the Congress the legislation will define the largest, most diversified outdoor recreation area in the United States. It will be within easy driving distance of millions of people.

You can personally help save wilderness from pollution because of these population pressures by urging congressional approval of this recreation pressure safety valve, and others like it. You have an opportunity to invest 15 cents for the future protection of wilderness. Buy three five-cent stamps and write your congressman and your two senators. Plead with them to approve this legislation and thereby make a beginning toward reducing the threat of devastation of wilderness and parks because sufficient alternative recreation areas do not now exist.

Let me say as an aside that I remember several years ago a very controversial bill that affected California within the field of water. There was a flood of letters that came to Washington, many of which I had to answer for various congressmen. But when the bill was passed, Congressman Engle, author of the legislation, did not receive a single letter of appreciation from a single person in California. This shows how quick we are to be against something, how quick to denounce it; but when we have a chance to be positive or to offer a word of praise when congressmen finish a job, how often we read about it in the paper, take credit for ourselves, and go on our merry way. If the wilderness group is going to be successful, you will have to learn this lesson in practical politics.

Another chance to provide more outdoor recreation opportunities in California which has been generally overlooked is contained in the legislation by Senator Thomas H. Kuchel and Congressman Harold T. Johnson to authorize Auburn Dam.

It would authorize a flood control and water conservation project that would bring water all along the eastern slope of the San Joaquin Valley. It would be tremendously helpful not only to flood control and water conservation, but would also be beneficial to wildlife and conservation.

The recreation aspect has not been emphasized. It will create 150 miles of shoreline on two branches of the attractive American River. It will provide 10,000 acres of lake close to Interstate Highway 80. It is time now that we think in terms of developing the recreational potential of this project.

I think we owe a vote of thanks to some of the private companies that are involved. The PG&E has launched a program in the last few years to develop the recreation potential of their power dams. They are doing a good job.

Edison Company in Southern California is doing an excellent job and has developed a camping area around Shaver Lake. The predecessor company in this field was the Portland General Electric, front runner in this whole area of using private funds to develop recreation potentials. It is good public relations; it is good for the areas involved; it creates a greater use of power.

The third and the last point I want to make is that unless we can create a national state of mind to abate pollution at "our front door" we cannot expect to save the wilderness from devastation.

Perhaps some of you noticed the Bill Mauldin cartoon the *San Francisco Chronicle* used to illustrate an article by Harold Gilliam, San Francisco's discerning disciple of the "Teachings of This Land."

The cartoon shows an industrial area with ugly buildings surmounted by a dozen stacks belching smoke into a blackened sky. In a grassless area bordered by dead snags that once were trees, two large pipes pour their dark putrefaction into a dried-up stream bed. The skeleton of a dead fish lies in the sand. On one of the tree stumps is a sign that says: "Danger! Pollution."

Off to one side is a promoter who, with loud mouth and a grand, sweeping gesture, is saying to his companion, "Just think, once this was nothing but raw wilderness."

There are so many examples of this, and this is really our basic problem. This is what I am talking about when I refer to our front door. There is not any area in the United States that has any more practical conservation challenges than the area right around the San Francisco Bay.

With respect to the Bay pollution threat, the San Luis Drain of the Central Valley Project, with an outlet at Antioch, has become the emotional symbol of befouled water. The real problem is much broader and has been building up to the present controversy for decades. A Bay Area population of four million now and predictions that it will be twice as great in a relatively few years make it impossible to look the other way, hoping the problem will go away. More and more people are concerned.

As Herb Caen remarked recently, even a new song has been produced that warns against the pollution of the Bay by fill and foul wastes. It goes:

> *What's that stinky creek out there—*
> *Down behind the slums' back stair?*
> *Sludgy puddle, sad and gray?*
> *Why, man, that's San Francisco Bay!*

It isn't that bad yet, but the people in the Bay Area must be especially alert or each individual group proposing unnecessary Bay fill will try to "get theirs" first.

One-third of the Bay has been filled since San Francisco's Palace Hotel was built. There are at least three dozen proposals for major fills in the Bay now. Bay fill which is not absolutely essential in the total public interest is another form of Bay pollution that will render its waters foul and unfit for full and proper use.

I realize there are those who say it can't happen here. Let's not forget that last summer one-fourth of beautiful Lake Erie, 2,600 square miles, was without sufficient dissolved oxygen to support life because of the pollution load from surrounding cities and adjacent countryside.

You, as others, want to know "what we can do." I have been asked that question with reference to the general problem and the San Luis Drain by Mayor John F. Shelley of San Francisco. I made some suggestions last month in response to his request outlining a three-point program to abate pollution. Since reviewing these, Mayor Shelley has suggested some changes in the three-point plan.

Mayor Shelley agrees we need some immediate legislative action. It must be action to protect the hard won gains of the San Joaquin Valley interests. Construction of the San Luis Drain must move forward or construction of a vitally-needed California water project will be held up. There must also be action designed to eventually authorize a waste disposal sewer for cities around the Bay. Some temporary outlet for the drain can buy time, but ultimately a permanent outlet for the drain must be built.

Specifically the Mayor suggests these changes in the earlier plan. He believes the Secretary of Defense should be included among the Cabinet officers who would report to the Congress as the Army and Navy have vital interests in the Bay. He believes the first report should be prepared in three years instead of five years as I originally suggested. Mayor Shelley believes that the "Johnson-Brown Commission" should have 15 members instead of nine. This, he points out, would permit three representatives each from the Congress and the State Legislature. This makes sense because they are the governmental bodies that will ultimately determine public policy.

So with those changes by Mayor Shelley, here is a three-point program to attack Bay Pollution:

1. Authorize construction of evaporating ponds in the San Joaquin Valley as a temporary disposal system for the early collection of water from the San Luis Drain.

2. Authorize an extension of the Master Drain from the evaporating ponds around the shores of the Bay to the Pacific Ocean; provided, however, that no construction funds shall be appropriated until:

(a) The Secretary of Defense, the Secretary of the Interior, the Secretary of Agriculture, and the Secretary of Health, Education, and Welfare report to the Congress on an acceptable plan of ocean-outlet development which plan shall be submitted not later than January 1969;

(b) The proposed plan shall be accompanied by comments, recommendations, and a State plan for Bay waste disposal from the Governor of California;

(c) The Cabinet Officers' report shall also be accompanied by comments and recommendations of the boards of supervisors of any counties in the Sacramento, San Joaquin, San Francisco Bay Area drainage area which counties officially declare a valid interest in the Master Drain to the Pacific Ocean.

3. Authorize a Federal-State Bay Area Pollution Abatement Commission of 15 members to meet periodically as a public forum for con-

sideration of drainage plans suggested by Federal, State, and local officials. Nine members shall be selected from a list of responsible citizens not regularly employed in Federal or State service. The President of the United States shall select five persons whose background qualifies them for exercising sound judgment in recommending a long-range pollution abatement program. Four others shall be selected by the Governor of California. The President shall select the chairman. The Commission shall also include three members of the State Legislature appointed by the Governor and three members of the Congress appointed by the President.

The Commission shall report to the President of the United States and the Governor of California not later than January 1, 1969. The Commission shall have furnished from appropriate State and Federal agencies at approximately equal cost such staff as may be required to conduct periodic hearings and prepare the necessary reports. Members of the Federal-State Commission shall serve without pay, but be reimbursed on a per diem basis while attending hearings.

That is the basic outline of a suggested approach. Doubtless others can refine and improve upon the proposal.

Now what would such legislative action accomplish? It would permit construction of a temporary disposal outlet for the drain and permit construction of the drain to continue. The drain is absolutely necessary in the long run. Without it the operation of the San Luis Project will certainly be delayed because of litigation. That would be an economic tragedy for California.

The legislative plan outlined would provide a means for determining the long-range drainage program of the Federal departments involved and the views of the State of California on the program. The plan would also define a method for obtaining the views of the cities and counties which are effected.

The plan now suggested by Mayor Shelley would let outside experts participate in solving the problem. Such a proposal would avoid putting the foxes in charge of protecting the hen house.

The three point plan would provide for periodic public hearings by a 15-man group. This would provide a forum essential to insuring public debate and dissemination of information as the long-range programs are formulated. A similar citizens group was appointed by Governor Rolph in 1931 which helped draft the initial plans for the Central Valley Project in California and brought a lot of the warring factions together.

Another group, the "Hoover-Young Commission," served some-what the same purpose. Later, a Federal-State group helped solve the Bay Bridge location problems. A Federal-State Commission, a so-called "Johnson-Brown Commission," could help protect the public interest in plans for a huge Bay Area drain to the Pacific Ocean.

In summary, then, I want to emphasize that you cannot save wil-derness from devastation without saving the beauty of America as a whole. We won't save wilderness from population pressure without alternative outdoor recreation development. We won't save wilder-ness from pollution unless we abate pollution at our front door.

If all this appears impossible, if numbers seem small and the forces of devastation seem overwhelmingly large—remember that reference by President Kennedy, speaking before the Irish Parliament, to the statement of George Bernard Shaw, who said:

"Other people see things and say, 'Why?' . . . But I dream things that never were and I say, 'Why not?' "

FROM THE DISCUSSION

James Bonner, Paul Brooks, A. J. Haagen-Smit

-» *T. Eric Reynolds, Chairman*

Dr. A. J. HAAGEN-SMIT: Through the use of his reasoning power, man has been able to conquer diseases and make himself virtually independent of the forces which make life a hard struggle for existence. But here Newton's classical third law of motion enters in, which states that for each action there is an equal but opposite reaction. The improved living conditions have resulted in an explosive growth of the population, and if the same law doesn't interfere again there will be only standing room for our offspring in less than a century. Already we begin to feel the pinch; fertile soil has been eroded by poor industrial practice and poisoned by the indiscriminate use of insect controlling chemicals. In some states several percent of the agricultural land can no longer be used for agricultural crops because its products, due to poisonous pesticides absorbed from the soil, do not pass food and drug inspection.

The water of our rivers has been used as a sewer for our cities and industries; fish population has become extinct in many of the smelly receptacles of our waste.

Our air has fared no better; it has been the seemingly infinite reservoir for all our emissions of unsightly smoke, toxic fumes, and gases. Most of us have worried about the effect upon the eyes and some other unpleasantness of this invisible garbage that we put in the air, and for years I have been preaching the advantages of breathing clean air. In this missionary work I am enthusiastically supported by students, and I find often some choice bits of information pinned on the bulletin board. The other day there was a clipping from the newspaper reporting on essays written by some grade school students on a recent plague of caterpillars in California. One student wrote, "Pests are a nuisance; worms, caterpillars, and other things interfere with a man being able to do as he pleases." And with a touch of genius he added as an afterthought, "Man is also a pest to other men and probably to all living things, too."

There was some remark made earlier about impractical professors and especially those who give their material in such a way that only the very select few can understand. I feel that I should not let this statement pass unchallenged, and I can best reply by quoting a poem by a professor in mathematics from the University of Oxford who was incensed about the very often lengthy discussion on perfectly obvious problems.

We know what does the damage and we know what isn't good.
But nothing's done because it's not completely understood.
We have the know-how and the wealth but do nothing until
Our view of life provides us also with determined will.
We're fallible, of course, but must we always gasp for breath
Until we fully understand the chemistry of death.
We want clean air you say: but face this damaging rebuff—
Till things are catastrophic you don't want it quite enough!

It is high time to use the brain power which led to the present era of high material standards of living, to see to it that the spring of our abundance doesn't dry up too soon. We owe it to future generations that we leave to them the resources in a form that they can maintain at least our present standards of affluence.

This means that any unnecessary waste and willful destruction of nature is a criminal act against our own flesh and blood. But this is not all; we have to give nature its chance to recover from the consequences of the conflict with the human race.

My experience with these problems has been mostly with the condition of the air. But I remember vividly how once as a graduate student I tried to make a systematic study of the oxygen content of the water in a branch of the Rhine River which ran through our town. The blackish liquid contained no free oxygen and no fish either; only some lowly organisms, such as bloodsuckers, and an assortment of rather unpleasant microorganisms seemed to be at home. My boat would carry me down the river, and a mile or two outside the city, the black water became transparent, the odor disappeared, and the fisherman sitting on his little chair on the tow path again became a part of the landscape. But this pleasing picture did not last very long. In a small village a chemical factory spilled its refuse, and gone were the fishes and back was the odor. This picture repeated itself a few dozen times before I had plotted the tragic afflictions of the once crystal clear, life-giving mountain brook.

We do not have to go back to my student days in my Old Country, for we can find similar examples right here. With the towns getting bigger, the suburbs getting more numerous, the poor rivers never recover, and brown and black they wind away through the country. Above the rivers hang greyish or brownish air filled with smokes and smells.

The time is gone when smoke stacks indicated prosperity; today a self-respecting community sees to it that no needless smokes and gases darken the sky and corrode the buildings. Such a community finds a reward in more and better business and in healthier and happier people.

It has been written that *our future security may depend less upon priority in exploring outer space than upon our wisdom in managing the space in which we live.*

Much progress has been made, but far more is still to be accomplished. The parks we set aside with some struggles have constantly to be defended against those who seem to be allergic to these open spaces and consider them ideal locations for freeways, schools, and so-called clean industries. The rules we set for standards of emissions for water quality control have to be fought for every inch of the way. Too often we do not have the needed information to come to any exact scientifically determined figure for safe community levels. In fact there is no such level at all. We must get used to the fact that industrial levels are not applicable to those for a community. These have to protect not only the healthy but also the young, old, and diseased. Economists point out that a standard involves a cost-benefit ratio. The greater the benefit in health or enjoyment of life, the greater the cost of correcting effluents or emissions. Our way of living does not set a dollar figure on the life of a human being. I am reminded of the wise diagnosis of the Greek philosopher, Hippocrates, who said, "That is best which is farthest removed from that which is unwholesome."

MODERATOR REYNOLDS: While we are talking about these things, we have a related question for you: "What about smog control through green belts, trees, and open spaces?"

DR. HAAGEN-SMIT: I am for green belts, but the trees are not high enough to take care of the situation. The atmosphere over Los Angeles is filled with pollutants up to about a thousand or two thousand feet, so a tree of some 50 feet is not going to do much about the general air pollution condition. Nevertheless, I believe that surrounding the house with a rather dense barrier of trees and bushes will help in diverting the smog. Some of the active components will react with vapors given off by the plants, and also absorption of such vapors on the plant surfaces takes place. There may be some damage to the leaves when they absorb the smog, but they will be replaced.

MODERATOR REYNOLDS: Here's another question: "In the total environment of everyday life, tobacco smoking plays a tremendous part in pollution of air in offices, in the streets, in public gatherings. Why is there so little recognition by our ardent conservationists that air with tobacco smoke in it is no longer fresh?"

DR. HAAGEN-SMIT: I used to be a smoker, but after I analyzed the smoke in the laboratory, I gave it up. Several years ago a lady asked me what she could do about the smog. I told her to go to the Air Pollution Control headquarters on Santa Fé Avenue and to put some pressure on the public officials. The answer was, "Oh, I'm not going down there again. When I was a block away I smelled the cigar smoke coming out of the place." The point is that there are a number of people who are quite sensitive to tobacco smoke, and to them the smoke-filled rooms are highly disagreeable.

I carried out some work on the chemical composition of cigar and cigarette smoke and found that the concentration of toxic components such as carbon monoxide and oxides of nitrogen is quite high. It is of the same order as in the exhaust of a car. The concentration of carbon monoxide is about two to four percent, or expressed in a different way, 20,000 to 40,000 parts per million. The lethal dose is around 500 to 1,000 parts per million. The only thing that saves the smoker is that he exposes himself intermittently to these high concentrations. Nevertheless, the one pack a day smoker inactivates about five percent of the oxygen-carrying capacity of his blood. Also well known is the smoker's cough due to the direct toxic action of the smoke constituents.

The amount of air drawn through a cigarette is about 500 milliliters. This smoky air would raise the carbon monoxide level of an ordinary living room by about one tenth of a part per million. This is nothing to worry about since the State Health Standard is about 30 parts per million for an eight-hour exposure. Nevertheless, there are toxic agents active at lower concentrations, and most nonsmokers have experienced the unpleasant irritation in smoke-filled rooms. It may be some consolation that the smoker himself receives the brunt of the punishment.

MODERATOR REYNOLDS: I remember not long ago when I was riding in a taxicab in Seattle, the driver apologized for the smog. I tried to reassure him that I was not upset at finding a little there. Then he told me that earlier in the summer he had visited Fairbanks and it had smog too. He had been reading the papers, and he said that this was feasible because of the long summer days and the elements that go to make up smog.

Since we are so interested in Alaska today, I wonder if you would comment on this: Is it possible to have smog in areas that have as short and intense a summer as Fairbanks?

DR. HAAGEN-SMIT: It is quite possible; the type of smog that we have in Los Angeles is not limited to that area. The same symptoms have been found in other cities, such as San Francisco, Cincinnati, and New York. Recently the tobacco fields downwind from Washington, D.C., were severely damaged by Los Angeles type smog. I assure you that it had not blown over from California. It brought home the fact that smog can be formed anywhere, and this realization was certainly a factor in the adoption of the Clean Air Act. All that is necessary to form smog is the release of large quantities of products of incomplete combustion, a stagnant atmosphere, and sunlight. Irritating products are formed in a relatively few minutes.

MODERATOR REYNOLDS: I have a question for Dr. Bonner: "In the New Stone Age, how are we going to mine the rocks for the energy yield, and just where are these rocks going to come from?"

DR. BONNER: As I said, in this New Stone Age we will work down on the surface only an average of a few millimeters of land surface per year. But instead of peeling the whole earth, we will, I imagine, take selected areas that are uninteresting for one reason or another, dig a big hole, processing the rock as we go. Then we will take the residue and put it back in the hole, and the hole will gradually move over the earth's surface, so we will never have a very deep mountain of residue that has been extracted. In this way we can at least minimize the upset of the earth's terrain by this very large mining operation.

Don't forget that already during the history of our present industrial, technological culture we have done a great deal of mining that has upset the earth's surface a great deal. We will be able to support our New Stone Age culture for some time—perhaps two or three generations—without disturbing the earth's surface any more than placer mining for gold has disturbed the earth's surface in the past.

MODERATOR REYNOLDS: There is another question: "How are you going to save the beaches and the sand dune wilderness areas as natural scientific research areas and as recreation areas and as scenic wilderness—for sand dunes are wilderness, too?"

DR. BONNER: This question is directed, I think, at the suggestion I made that our large all-purpose plants would be situated on the ocean, so they can have ready access to ocean water. I would think that the way to have our plants situated on the ocean and at the same time preserve the beaches would be to put these plants where there are presently unpleasant looking facilities on the ocean, tear down the old-fashioned power plants and replace them by these new nuclear-powered plants. As a matter of fact, I can think of quite a few other things along the ocean front—in Southern California, for example, rows of people's houses. Although it is natural that some people want to live near the ocean, I think I would rather tear down a few houses and replace them by my all-purpose chemical plant and in return create public beaches. In any case, in the future I think we have to use a small portion of the beach for our industrial technological culture, but I don't think it will be so bad. We already use a part of the beach area, and I think that in time we can perhaps use even a smaller proportion of it.

MODERATOR REYNOLDS: We will go on to some questions for Mr. Brooks. There is one here that says: "What can this group do to discourage the Rampart Dam? When will this decision come up for action?"

MR. BROOKS: To take the second question first, the last I heard, it is supposed to be included in the so-called "Omnibus Bill for 1966"; that is when it will come up.

As to what one can do, since this is a matter Congress will decide, the form of action would be very much the same as the action on any Congressional Bill that you are interested in—in terms of getting in touch with your senator and your congressman and so on.

MODERATOR REYNOLDS: Another question for Mr. Brooks says: "In that Rampart Dam is in a perma-frost area, what would be the effect of the increase in population in the dam area?" Assuming, I suppose, that the power is used to dissipate perma-frost, if that is possible.

MR. BROOKS: It is, of course, in the perma-frost area. I have not thought in terms of the use of power to dissipate perma-frost, I don't know enough about this technically. I know one thing that can happen. There is a roadhouse called The Inn along the Alaskan Highway. They got very modern and they put central heating in the cellar, and this quite unintentionally dissipated the perma-frost to the extent of about six inches a year, and now it is way below ground level and you have to go down a long ramp to get into the door. So I don't think there will be much of an attempt to dissipate perma-frost. The owners of most of these buildings will make sure that you don't melt the ice.

As for the increase in population, people who have studied the subject feel that the growth of population will be in the southern part of Alaska. A city like Fairbanks, which is in the north central part of the State, is going to grow very slowly and probably will not become a great industrial city. Its main importance will be as a communications center, and therefore I doubt whether predictions of great population growth in that part of the State are justified.

MODERATOR REYNOLDS: One other on the subject of Rampart: "Assuming that Rampart's real justification is a means of pouring Federal funds into Alaska, is it politically impractical to propose comparable Federal subsidies to local hydroelectric projects or to support schools, roads, parks, recreational facilities, and other such things, which would spread the benefits of the money to all parts of Alaska? In other words, offering a substitute pork barrel?"

MR. BROOKS: I think that is a very constructive question. Surely this sort of thing, in the opinion of most conservationists, is an infinitely better idea. If we must have WPA projects, let us not have the kind that destroy the countryside. I should think the necessity for bolstering the State's economy is a philosophical question—how much the Federal Government should back up the State.

The argument of YPA, I think, against these local projects—I have never asked any official this question—is that you get the votes for one, great, big, glamorous project. I have tried to stress the fact that Rampart Dam is a promotor's dream from its very beginning. These promotors are worried about smaller things like Devil's Canyon. One person said, "Yes, it might work, but let's take the big one."

MODERATOR REYNOLDS: Let's turn to Dr. Bonner for a few minutes again. There is a question here that says: "Dr. Bonner, your picture of the exhaustion of petroleum, coal, et cetera, and the splendid coincidence of the discovery of nuclear power appears to fit a standard picture of a species eating itself to death. Can we not hope for a prior re-evaluation of our 'culture' so that there is no necessity for this auto-cannibalism? What about radioactive waste? Any comment on this?"

DR. BONNER: This question is from a person who believes, like so many people do, that, "Oh, gee whiz, couldn't we go back to the good old days and a simpler life? Couldn't we abolish all these frills and luxuries and just take the real necessities of life?" Well, it is a beautiful thought. The trouble is that the luxuries of today have a way of turning into necessities of tomorrow. Suppose that you define as a necessity of life anything that would make the death rate rise if it were abolished from our culture. I think that is fair enough—anything that is going to make you less likely to die is a necessity. We want to abolish luxuries, but measured by this criterion, the telephone, which a generation ago was a luxury, has now become a necessity. If you abolished the telephone, the death rate would go up; nobody could call the doctor. Even the automobile is a necessity; for horrible as it may seem today, I am sure if you abolished automobiles all over the United States, the death rate would rise. For one thing, lots of people would starve to death; we couldn't carry food around from one place to another, because our transport system is zeroed in on the automobile.

I think it is a hallucination to think that we can—at least with the present population of the United States—go back to a simpler life. The most we can hope to do is to minimize the rate at which its complexity increases.

The second part—what to do about the nuclear waste. I made a suggestion about that down in Texas when I was talking about this general subject. I suggested that by the time we get to using atomic power on a large scale, all the oil wells in Texas will be dry, so we just pour that radioactive waste down their oil wells. I thought it was a very reasonable suggestion, but it didn't go over very well down there.

There was a point I would like to comment on. This question is, "In terms of changing the surface of the earth, what is the difference between building a high dam and in building an enormous rock processing plant?" Well, the difference is that if you are going to build a high dam you've got to build it where that river is, you see; but if you're going to go on a rock grinding binge, you can pick the spot and leave the river the way it was. So I think that all of us would feel much happier to not build high dams and leave our canyons as they are, and choose some sites—each of us could nominate one— which would be the first to be ground up. My nominee would be the heart of some old and dilapidated, slummy city.

IV

BANQUET
April 2, 1965

Presentation of the John Muir Award
WILLIAM E. SIRI

Introduction
CLARK KERR

Address
CLINTON P. ANDERSON

WILLIAM E. SIRI, *Master of Ceremonies*

The Fifth Annual John Muir Award

1965

Presented by the Sierra Club to

Francis P. Farquhar

⚘ In gratitude for the superior quality of his contributions toward preserving unspoiled a living part of the American heritage of wilderness

⚘ In recognition of the excellence of his thinking and writing and leading, about mountains and in them, but especially in the Sierra Nevada, that we believe will truly make a difference a hundred years from now in the face of this land

⚘ And in appreciation of the warmth and the friendship with which he has carried out his role in assuring that America will remain more beautiful than it otherwise could have been for those who come after us.

His achievement carries forward the historic work of John Muir in rescuing for our time those primeval places epitomized in the great national parks.

WILLIAM E. SIRI

President

for the Committee on the John Muir Award

Facsimile of award presented at the conference

INTRODUCTION

→» *Clark Kerr*

All of us in the San Francisco Bay Area are delighted that the Wilderness Conference is meeting here once again—to have you here talking about one of the most important issues for the future of the United States.

Man is, of course, taking over and dominating his environment. There was a time when man preserved himself rather precariously within an environment given by nature, but now he is in a way destroying nature and creating his own environment. And one wonders sometimes whether man really will be able to survive as well in the man-made environment as he did in the environment made by nature.

There are all kinds of predictions of how the world is going to end, with all the trees chopped down and great concrete highways and freeways all over the place.

A few years ago on the Berkeley campus I was given the opportunity to introduce Sir Charles Darwin, the grandson of the author of *The Origin of Species.* He himself had just written a rather famous book, looking to the future of the world. He called it *The Next Million Years,* and he said that nobody can know what is going to happen in the next hour, the next week, the next year, the next century, the next thousand years, but certainly we are going to know what happens in the next million years.

He pictured a world in which all the natural resources had been destroyed and there were just a very few people left on this depleted planet; where life had reverted to the situation which Thomas Hobbs described so long ago—"solitary, poor, nasty, brutish, and short." And so in introducing him, I described a couple of visions of my own of the end of the world when man should come to dominate it completely.

Just a few days before, I had gone to our Richmond Field Station and had seen some work being done there with algae tanks. I was told by the professors working upon them that this really was the future. You put sewage in one end and you have the algae cooking in the sun, and you drink the water that comes out the other end, as one of the professors did. He offered me the opportunity, but not being thirsty at the time, I declined. These algae would supply all the food that man needed. So I saw the future of the world; it was the most efficient way for man to live. The whole world was covered with algae tanks, with little colonies on top of them, the algae cooking in the sun in this self-restoring process. There wasn't any point going back into history. As far back as anybody knew there had been algae tanks; as far as anybody could see ahead, algae tanks and more algae tanks. In traveling all around the world, nothing but algae tanks every place.

Then I came across another piece of information which really startled me, and I got a different vision of the end of the world. I was told by our librarian in his argument for more and more books that with each sixteen years the number of titles of books in the world doubled. This is not the number of copies—that goes up much faster—and you can project this increase for centuries and thousands of years into the future. Everybody knows what happens once a librarian gets a catalogue, and I saw the end of the world not as algae tanks every place but rather as one vast library, until there were only three people left in the world. And the third-from-the-last person was a university professor who wrote the last book ever to be written; the second-from-the-last person was the printer who printed it; and the last person was the librarian who took this book, put it on the last empty place on the last empty shelf, and then, in the self-effacing manner of librarians, committed suicide. Man had created his own environment and had failed to survive.

We do have to maintain, as all of you know so well, the environment that nature gave us, and I would like before introducing Senator Anderson to say just a few words about the interest of the University of California in all of this.

We have recently established a Wildland Research Center, as some of you may know, under Professor Henry J. Vaux of our School of Forestry, to be concerned with the preservation and care of the wildlands of the State of California.

We recently established near Palm Desert through the gift of one of our Regents, Philip Boyd, a great desert research center, reserving a whole canyon—its floor and up to the heights of the mountains where wild sheep are still found.

We are also now engaged in a new program, which I placed before the Regents recently and which was adopted unanimously by them—the Land and Water Reserves Program. This program will try to identify in this very diversified State the major ecological areas, from the ocean to the High Sierra, the deserts, the forests, the marsh lands, etc., and also will try through the University of California to preserve in perpetuity at least one representative sample of each of the different ecological areas of the State of California for the sake of research and for the sake of generations of students to come.

This may be one of the last chances we have to do this, as the population grows and grows in the State of California. It is a program in which we want your assistance, the assistance of the State of California, the assistance of the Federal Government.

We are also trying to develop on our Riverside campus a great concentration on the study of air, land, and water, and on the use of these great resources and their conservation. And in many other ways the University of California is trying to contribute to the understanding and the preservation of the natural resources of this State.

I should like to depart for just a moment from the role of speaking as the President of the University of California and speak, rather, as the husband of my wife. She would want me to say—in fact she encouraged me to say—that we have here in the great metropolitan San Francisco Bay Area, a wonderful wilderness right at its center—a wilderness which largely maintains itself, which returns revenue to the surrounding areas, which is a thing of beauty. And in trying to preserve the wilderness areas of the state and the nation, one of the great places to start would be to save San Francisco Bay for the enjoyment and the contemplation of millions of people.

Our chief speaker this evening is one of the key lawmakers who has been involved in the passage of Federal legislation to preserve our great national heritage. He described the evolution of his interest in legislation for the preservation of wilderness and seeking wilderness areas in a very interesting speech last November before the Rio Grande Chapter's Natural Area Conference in Santa Fe. He notes that it was the public's demonstrated interest in conservation that stimulated his own interest, and thus helped bring about the unprecedented burst of conservation legislation enacted by the 88th Congress.

Clinton P. Anderson has been United States Senator from New Mexico since 1948. Before that he served as Secretary of Agriculture in the cabinet of President Truman. He was a member from New

Mexico at Large of the 77th, 78th, and 79th Congresses. He was Treasurer of New Mexico in 1933 and 1934. He has also worked in the insurance business and as a newspaperman.

It is one of my pleasant duties this evening to present him with an Honorary Life Membership in the Sierra Club in recognition of his many contributions to the cause to which the club is dedicated. This is one of the club's highest honors, is bestowed on very few people, and is given only for outstanding service. I am happy to confer it now on our speaker for the evening, Senator Anderson.

ADDRESS

→→→ *Clinton P. Anderson*

I very much appreciate this high honor. It indicates to me that hard work is recognized sometimes in the organizations for which we work. As President Kerr has stated, this is my second appearance at a Sierra Club event within five months.

Tonight—as then—I feel at home among old friends, among comrades in arms in the long struggle to save wilderness America.

Those who roam the wilderness years from now will marvel at its quiet and its charm. But they may neither remember nor appreciate what organizations like the Sierra Club and The Wilderness Society did to preserve it. Those of us who do, however, will remain forever grateful.

Together with its allies in the conservation movement, the Sierra Club came to Congress again and again and again to plead the cause of wilderness preservation. National attention was centered on the need to endow future generations with an inheritance of the land— land with a wild beauty as yet unscarred by man; land remote in mood and location but accessible to those who want to experience the wilderness.

After eight years of hearings, reports, debates, and off-stage conversations, we have at last created a Wilderness System. No one man, no single group was responsible for that historic achievement. But Vice President Hubert Humphrey blazed the trail in Congress by introducing the original Wilderness Bill—and in the highest administrative circles, he will be among our allies. The roll of honor includes the late Senator James Murray of Montana, his successor, Lee Metcalf; Senators Frank Church and Tom Kuchel, and Congressmen Wayne Aspinall and John Saylor, to name but a few. It also includes Aldo Leopold and Howard Zahniser, who are no longer with us, and Dave Brower, who very much is.

There will be other heroes. For the long struggle to save something of America's wilderness for our children did not end with the passage of a law. The next few years will be crucial. They will tell how well we succeed in creating a Wilderness System under an Act we finally accepted, though it is considerably less than we would have liked.

The Interior Department is reviewing all roadless areas of 5,000 acres or more in the National Park System and similar areas regardless of size in the wildlife preserves and game ranges. The Department of Agriculture is reviewing some 5½ million acres of Primitive Areas in the national forests. These surveys, over a ten-year period, are in accord with the Wilderness Act's provision for the submission to Congress of proposed new areas for inclusion in the Wilderness System.

We need, however, to look beyond these areas specified for potential preservation in the Wilderness Act. Those who forced us to compromise did not intend to make it easy to save additional land for coming generations. We are going to have to justify each additional Wilderness Area, beyond the 9.1 million acres of the original Wilderness Act.

One of the most promising attempts to supplement the Wilderness Act—an effort that deserves the warm support of conservationists everywhere—is the Wild Rivers Act, introduced in Congress this year.

This Act "finds that some of the free-flowing rivers of the United States possess unique water conservation, scenic, fish, wildlife, and outdoor recreation values of present and potential benefit to the American people."

Congress would be given the power to designate such unspoiled river sections—in sparsely populated areas, near the sources of the rivers, and above any dam sites—as wild river areas, to be administered for present and future generations by the departments of Interior and Agriculture. Six river segments are so named in the Act, and nine others are listed for study in the Act.

Some critics of the Wild Rivers Act wonder what effect it will have on flood control. If dam construction is prohibited in wild river areas as a hindrance to the free flowing of the river segment, won't these segments be susceptible to damaging floods?

One of the best answers to this question was given in a letter written me two weeks ago by the Sierra Club's vice president, Dr. Edgar Wayburn. He pointed out that damming in only one way—and a comparatively expensive way—would cut down flood damage. It is, of course, the only way in the more heavily developed, populated areas.

But, as Dr. Wayburn points out, there may be another way to minimize flood damage in wild river areas. That way is to protect the river from wastes and debris caused by industry, logging, or mining. This is one of the things that the Wild Rivers Act may accomplish.

Dr. Wayburn claims—and I think he is correct—that much of the damage caused by the flood disasters out here last December came because of silt and logging debris that hindered the water from returning to its natural level.

The Wild Rivers Act will cut down flood damage. It will not interfere with dam building in populated areas where such work is appropriate.

The Wild Rivers Act is at once a conservation bill, a recreation bill, and a flood control bill. It deserves to be passed, and my hope is that everyone within the sound of my voice will support it.

This has been a profitable period for those who love good books on the out-of-doors, and I am collecting a five-foot shelf of conservation classics. On the shelf sits Rachel Carson's *Silent Spring,* Stewart Udall's *The Quiet Crisis, Resources in America's Future* by Landsberg, Fischman and Fisher, *Whose Woods These Are* by Michael Frome, *The Last Redwoods* by Hyde and Leydet, *Tomorrow's Wilderness* by Leydet, and, finally, a lovely volume, *"In Wildness is the Preservation of the World."*

Last year onto that shelf went Harold Barnett and Chandler Morse's new look at the prospects for natural resources. They found that, except for timber products, technology has made possible the production of commodities of every sort more cheaply and with less effort than in the past. Technology has also made it possible to discover new mineral deposits, to utilize lower grade ores, and to create substitutes, such as plastics.

Local pressure for economic development may prove to be the gravest threat to the preservation of unspoiled areas in the years just ahead. It always will be difficult to persuade a community that a nearby resource should be left undeveloped or held in reserve because there is abundance elsewhere.

Consequently, it seems to me that it is especially important that conservationists seek enlightened solutions to conflicts over land use and encourage application of the most improved technology to resource problems.

Some 52 million acres of accessible forest lands in the nation are now idle. Planted to trees, this acreage could produce at least 12 times as much timber as the inaccessible wilderness areas. But insects, fire, disease, and other hazards cost the commercial timberlands 4 billion board feet annually—80 times the growth capacity of the wilderness forests and nearly equivalent to our present annual timber cut.

There would be far less pressure on timber in wilderness if that potential production were realized. It would be farsighted for those who want to preserve an adequate amount of wilderness and scenic beauty to put full timber production potential on their agenda.

I know that you want the timber production to be conducted without disruption of watersheds. Dr. Wayburn made that dramatically clear in his letter. He showed how large logging operations and shortsighted land practices contributed to the flood devastation.

While the road ahead is difficult, I believe a good beginning has been made because there is wider acceptance that—in the words of Mr. Justice Douglas—"The esthetic values of the wilderness are as much our inheritance as the veins of copper and gold in our hills and the forests in our mountains."

Most people who use the wilderness live in cities. And while it is true that most of these areas are far from the heavy concentration of population in the East, it is also true that 16 Wilderness and Primitive Areas are within a few hours' drive of large urban centers in California.

The conservation movement is moving to town—and it is high time.

I was born in South Dakota before the turn of the century; and in that day seven out of ten Americans lived in rural areas. Now 70 percent of us live in areas having an urban density of 1,500 persons per square mile. A generation from now three of every four Americans will be city dwellers.

For these, it is not enough to have magnificent national parks and forests in the Far West. There is a growing nationwide demand for natural areas of rest and recreation. Recognition of this is apparent in the President's proposal for six new parks, lakeshores, recreation areas, and seashores east of the Mississippi River.

We must never forget that the fight to preserve beauty and cut down on pollution is national, not regional. We shall always cherish the memory of those great inspirers of conservation movements from the East: Theodore Roosevelt of New York, Gifford Pinchot of Pennsylvania, and John Kennedy of Massachusetts—tall men who stood tall.

President Johnson has declared his intention to use revenue from the Land and Water Conservation Fund to acquire lands needed to bring the proposed Eastern parklands into being.

Much of the value of the Land and Water Conservation Fund—which became law last fall—will stem from its application to metropolitan areas. "Give priority attention," the President said, "to serving the needs of our growing urban population." Conservation Fund dollars will be used to acquire desperately needed recreation areas for urban and suburban residents. It should not be necessary for families in cities to have to embark on an expedition to see a stand of trees or a grassy field.

There is a tendency, however, to regard the Fund as primarily for the massive park programs. Those who do should recall that the Federal portion of the Fund shall be used to obtain inholdings within Wilderness Areas of the National Forest System and to acquire areas for the preservation of species of fish or wildlife threatened with extinction. The state portions will be used to obtain state parklands and the urban and suburban recreation areas.

Money is already accumulating to get the Conservation Fund on its way. One source of revenue is the sale of recreation conservation automobile stickers. It is estimated that these stickers will net the Fund $35 million this year. I have one on my bumper—Number 13 for good luck. And I wish the sticker sale good luck too; because if sales fall short of expectations, the idea of the recreationist paying for a substantial part of the benefits he receives will go down the drain.

I want to say something on a number of parks proposed now. For some strange reason, I don't know what it is, numbers of senators are rushing in and they say, "I have to have a national park in my state and conservation."

In this Conservation Fund, we have brought together a variety of needs—those of the wilderness people, the wildlife enthusiasts, and the fellow who simply wants a refreshing place to sit down or hike right around home. It is meaningful that visitors to the great parks, sweeping oceanside areas, and lonely game preserves will—through their entrance fees—help provide themselves and neighbors in town with outdoor recreation sites.

A national policy has been laid down to acquire recreation lands. The Conservation Fund gives us the means for financing this ambitious program. But we need to move quickly, to act at the floodtide of public support.

Some seashores still remain—by good fortune—for potential inclusion in the national park system: Assateague in Maryland and Virginia, Oregon Dunes in Oregon, and Cape Lookout in North Carolina. And on the Great Lakes, there is the promise of public ownership for Sleeping Bear and Indiana Dunes.

Crowded recreation facilities and advancing bulldozers and developers have frightened the people and made it possible to win support in recent years for new recreation and wilderness facilities.

We have—as a nation—paid attention to resource problems on a crisis basis. We are alerted to the water crisis, the timber crisis, the pesticide crisis, the strip mine crisis. I have no question that it is the constant squeaking crisis that gets the oil. But is it the wisest way for a nation to develop and manage its resources for 190 million today and 330 million by the year 2000? I think not.

A Council of Resource and Conservation Advisers might help to avoid the potential wastefulness of reaction only in the face of crisis. It might enable decision-makers to take more initiative in advance of a severe resource problem rather than after it has ballooned to massive proportions.

The Council would be an arm of the Executive Branch, but it would serve all of government in much the same fashion as the Council of Economic Advisers. The Council of Economic Advisers does not create national economic policy, but it gathers the information and does the advance thinking essential to the shaping of enlightened policy. It is still up to political leaders to create and implement tax and fiscal policy. By the same token, members of Congress and Cabinet officers would still be left with the responsibility to make sound conservation policy.

The need for such a continuing high-level examination of natural resource matters was in the mind of the National Academy of Sciences when it recently said:

> . . . it is evident that optimization of natural resources for human use and welfare cannot be achieved by fragmentary and sporadic attention given to isolated parts of the problem but that the issues involved must be made the subject of a permanent, systematic process of investigation, recording, and evaluation, carried on continuously in reference to the total perspective.

This kind of evaluation should be applied to all decisions affecting natural resources—particularly when they are irretrievably lost, once used, or altered by man. The proposed high dams on the Lower Colorado River are a case in point. Before more dams are authorized, some of us want to be sure and know if the power to be produced is really economic and necessary or whether it is included as a way which has worked elsewhere and may now be the only way to finance the Central Arizona Project.

The most desperately needed resource in the Colorado River Basin is water itself. Some experts are advising storage in aquifers in that area to avoid losses to wind and sun.

The economics for further storage of surface water for power—even in relatively narrow reservoirs—is open to serious question, even without a charge for evaporation and recognizing that water has certain peaking capacity values over other sources of power.

The closest kind of study should be devoted to a detailed comparison of alternative energy sources for generating electricity. The Four Corners region of New Mexico, Arizona, Colorado, and Utah is underlaid with large deposits of coal. Some of that mineral abundance is now being used to generate electricity at quite favorable costs. There are other proposals in the talking stage for additional coal-fired plants at the mineheads of the Southwest.

While conservationists may look upon coal as a bulwark against encroachment on the Grand Canyon, they rebel against its use to produce kilowatts at certain other places. The banks of the St. Croix River are echoing to the sounds of battle between those who want the economic advantages of a large coal-burning electric plant and those who fear the blighting of one of our loveliest spring-fed rivers.

Jobs and a bigger tax base are tangible—a community can measure and feel that income. But what of the so-called intangibles—a clear stream for fishing or boating or just for looking at. They become less intangible when measured against the cost of restoration.

If coal barges, slag piles, and warm water from the plant will despoil the river, is there an alternative that will give the area electricity and payrolls without scenic and recreation damage? An atomic reactor offers a possible answer. It would avoid ugly slag heaps, high stacks, and barge traffic. It would not pollute the atmosphere, and it might be possible to avoid heating the river water. I think you are going to find that atoms for conservation make sense in many situations.

I was interested to read in the *Bulletin of the Atomic Scientists* the account of the fight over the Bodega Head power reactor. Your club had something to do with the withdrawal of the reactor project. Unequipped with all the details of that dispute, I would not attempt to plead the case for either side.

But I would counsel you not to reject nuclear reactors in all cases out of a fear that these power plants can behave like bombs or that they will spew radioactive wastes into the atmosphere. Rather, I would hope that the Sierra Club and other conservation groups will view the atom as an ally in the cause of intelligent resource development. ". . . Not blind opposition to progress, but opposition to blind progress . . ." is a principle that may serve us well in this matter.

While I have been close to the conservation movement for many years, I have long had a continuing involvement with atomic energy. I am optimistic about the alliance of the atom and conservation. Linked with desalinization plants, atomic energy will help provide additional water. In some areas, atomic power may lessen the need to lay bare hillsides to get at coal seams. Reactors will firm up hydropower so that large volumes of water do not waste into the sea without being productive. Atomic fuel will lessen air-polluting smog. And atomic energy can extend the fossil-fuel resources of the country.

Albert Schweitzer has said, "Man can hardly even recognize the devils of his own creation." But I believe that we are coming to recognize the problems posed by rapidly advancing technology. Like the genie in the lamp, technology can be used to enhance the quality of life or leave it barren. We will seek its blessings.

I foresee an intensification of the conflicts between what some call progress with a capital "P" and others call progress with a question mark. We are going to hear more and more about "Payrolls or Picnickers?" In the cities and the suburbs the road builders who want to pave over woodlands and level neighborhoods are racing with those who would ask: "Is there a better way to move people in metropolis?"

As I suggested in Sante Fe last fall, "All the angels are not on the side of the conservationists." But these problems demand our concern; how they are resolved will determine to a large extent the character and atmosphere of American life for generations.

Although the battle must be waged wilderness by wilderness, river by river, park by park, we must see conservation in its total dimensions. We must master technology for the broadest common good. We must improve the system of decision-making as regards resources.

"Those who will not remember the past," said Santayana, "are condemned to relive it."

But we do remember: how one landscape has been torn and defaced in the name of industry while another has been preserved for posterity almost as the Lord left it a long time ago. We remember the struggles to bring beauty to our cities, to save beauty along our shores, and to find beauty in the depths of a quiet forest where no tree has fallen save as the Master has decreed. Surely in this conference we can agree that no great problem is settled until it is settled right, and holding that belief, can dedicate ourselves "To the cause that needs assistance . . . And the good that we can do."

V

THE OUTLOOK FOR WILDERNESS

———————————

Keynote Address: The Outlook for Wilderness

PAUL B. SEARS

The Impact of Recent Legislation on Administrative Agencies

EDWARD P. CLIFF
EDWARD C. CRAFTS
GEORGE HARTZOG, JR.
CHARLES H. STODDARD

Wilderness—The Citizen's Evaluation

ALBERT LEPAWSKY

WILLIAM E. SIRI: *Chairman*

KEYNOTE ADDRESS:
THE OUTLOOK FOR WILDERNESS

➤➤➤ *Paul B. Sears*

The United States owes an immense debt to those of its citizens who, at the western boundary of our continent, determined to preserve as much as possible of its fabulous natural beauty. But to solve any problem requires us to see it in the broadest possible perspective. Preservation or, where that is no longer possible, restoration of natural conditions, is a need that pervades every section of our nation.

We face a choice between health and disease of the total landscape. My own observations have long convinced me that—on economic grounds alone—between 20 and 25 percent of our country's space should be maintained in its native cover. So it was gratifying to learn recently that this judgment had been quite precisely anticipated a century ago by the erudite scholar, traveler, and naturalist, George Perkins Marsh, in his classic *Man and Nature*.

It is cold comfort, but comfort nevertheless, to see official recognition of the fact that far too much land has been ripped up and exploited in the interest of what has turned out to be inefficient production. We can only hope that this will help us protect the good that is left and rebuild the remainder.

Any successful campaign requires realistic knowledge of the obstacles to be dealt with. The obstacles in our way as we work for a truly sound ecosystem are quite definite, quite general. Many of them have already been brought to the attention of this conference, but this does not deter me from a brief review.

Caricature is a powerful weapon, whether it takes shape on paper or in the popular mind. The conservationist gets his share of it. The opposition paints him as a wild-eyed sentimentalist, a "dickey-bird watcher," and "one of the bugs and bunny crowd."

To give an example, when the Yale Conservation Program was announced in 1950, President Griswold received a prompt call from a powerful alumnus whose industry was in the field of natural resources. The alumnus inquired with some heat, "What kind of a long-hair is in charge of this program?" A dinner was shortly arranged for us to meet. He not only saw that I visited my barber dutifully, but that I appreciated the problems of modern industry and respected the need for a truly sound and permanent economy. And while his corporate activities do not completely escape criticism, I have been fairly gratified by what I have observed of its subsequent trend.

Caricature is, of course, two-edged. In the hands of the late Ding Darling, it was a powerful influence for conservation. Clumsily used in the first attempts to discredit Rachel Carson, it revealed the weakness of the case against her. I know how she labored to be as certain as possible of her facts, although I feel, as I noted in a review for the *Washington Post,* that she would have strengthened her position by giving more space to the benefits that have been, and could be, derived from the advance of chemical knowledge.

By no means all of the difficulties we encounter come from without. Our very commitment to an urgent and critical cause carries with it a heavy emotional charge. It is easy to neglect the axiom of Sir Rufus Isaacs, the great British lawyer, who explained that he won his cases by means of what he called "deadly fair play."

Irresponsible and ill-informed evangelism is bound to react powerfully against those who employ it. Nothing does more damage to the prudent management of space and other natural resources than the eloquence of an advocate who doesn't know what he is talking about. He should be armed with a respect for scientific accuracy, and a realistic appreciation of legitimate conflicts of interest.

Certainly our efforts on behalf of a truly healthy landscape must be dramatized. This is why the role of the artist, which the Sierra Club employs with such consummate skill, is vital. So is the enlistment of the entire range of human talent that can be brought to bear. Our campaign has not only its ethical and esthetic factors, but its legal, financial, technological, educational, and political components as well. There is no place for ignorance or naïveté, either with respect to physical fact or the merits of any opposition.

Science, viewed in its totality, is on our side. All the rules of experience that have to do with energetics, material change and recycling, and population dynamics support the need for a generous and rational design of the landscape. Whether or not all individual scientists see this, we must remember that science has its camp followers, often a vocal lot. Many of them are so impressed with the marvelous advances in science and technology that they bestow upon these modern twins the faith once reserved for deity. Either they become quite relaxed about the destiny of man or they propose a Utopia of completely controlled mechanization. This new religion, ranging from acquiescence to aggression, is one of our toughest problems.

One of its most dangerous by-products is the confusion of growth with health. These, as any biologist knows, are two very different phenomena. Growth, whether of size or numbers, is a determinate process, self-limiting. Otherwise, it exceeds the capacity of organization and becomes pathological. I am immensely disturbed to see the vitality of the American nation measured only by the growth of the Gross National Product, the expansion of urban industry, or the avalanche of new customers.

We are confronted with such banal slogans as, "You can't stop progress," and "Prosperity depends upon the baby crop." Change can certainly not be stopped, but it should, in this age of science, be guided. We cannot win our objectives unless we are concerned to see that population does not get out of bounds. If it does, nothing can spare us from the fate of China, where the few surviving specimens of the original plant life have had to be preserved in temple grounds. We must do all we can to promote a general sense of responsibility for the control of population increase.

The Japanese have already set us an example. In our own country it is encouraging to see the population problem discussed with a frankness and a concern never before possible. Let us hope that it will become a point of national honor that no child shall enter the world unless he is truly welcome and has a fair chance for a good life as he grows up.

Quite as important as the mere number of human beings is their distribution. Here the accepted formula seems to be that we must continue to get men and women off the land and into our great urban industrial centers, already suffering from acute cultural gastritis.

To the degree that this unbalanced distribution comes about, the tenuous bonds between humanity and the rest of the natural world will be further weakened. Open space that might be available for preservation or restoration will be increasingly consumed by the expansion of dwellings, industries, highways, and all the other accessories of so-called civilization. As this goes on, the objectives to which this conference is dedicated will recede to the vanishing point.

This situation is exemplified in today's agriculture, a tortured problem and one which bears upon the reservation of natural areas. It is now possible for individuals who have accumulated great wealth from industry, coal, or oil to purchase very large acreages and set themselves up in mass production of meat or grain crops. Favorable legislation plus command of capital give them a great advantage over the small farmer. I recently learned of one instance in which thousands of acres, including miles of fine stream previously open to the public, had passed into a single such unit.

Many, if not all economists, pronounce this trend as inevitable. Even official policy hints strongly that the solution to the farm problem lies in moving men and women off of small family farms into industrial centers and finding work for them there. The stock assumption is that since the small farm does not pay in the conventional sense, it must go. Along with this goes another assumption, evident in some branches of chemical industry, automobile design, TV programming, adventure in space, and, I fear, in the immense industries which are related to agriculture. This is the tenet that whatever becomes technologically possible, is therefore justified.

I do not know the prevailing opinion among sociologists, if they hold one. Even the layman knows that we owe much to the family farm. While I have nothing that can be fed into a computer, I have made it a point in recent years to discuss matters with other veterans who have taught during most of two generations. All agree that, by and large, boys and girls with a rural background have a stronger motivation and greater sense of responsibility than the average.

Here the remark of a Scottish marine engineer is apropos. Asked to explain the remarkable record of Scotsmen in many professions over the world, he replied, "It's their strict up-bringin' does it. Many an auld Scot is dead and in his grave before the son ever guesses how much the auld man loved him." And this is a proper place to stress one of the great values of wilderness experience as a training for youth. It is high time we devise some way to balance the quick and obvious profits from rival forms of land use against the benefits to boys and girls who have learned to know and enjoy unspoiled nature at first hand. Here again I speak from long personal observation.

Easily three quarters of our local television and radio news for the past two months has consisted of a monotonous recital of serious crimes committed by urban youth. We know this to be true because the street addresses of the young malefactors are given. The proposal to continue crowding still more families into this vortex of cultural indigestion as a solution of the farm problem makes no sense to me. Neither does the persistent gnawing away at what remains of the unspoiled out-of-doors, not to mention the continuing invasion of urban parks and local green spaces. I regret to say that some universities that should understand the value of green laboratories, even if they are insensitive to esthetics, have much to answer for in this respect.

I have spoken of cultural indigestion. This, no transient social belly-ache, has reached morbid proportions. For almost a million years humanity has lived in a world of slow, almost imperceptible change. As its groups spread out to all of the continents and the varied habitats in each, there was time to fit custom, belief, and sanction to living conditions. This gave to simple societies some measure of certainty and control, however strange their patterns may seem to us.

Repeatedly, however, as civilizations developed and populations increased, so did pressures within and without. Old systems of values and controls disintegrated, environments were depleted and civilizations came apart. None, however, were the victims of such rapid changes as ours.

We have an advantage they did not possess, thanks to our knowledge of the physical world and of history. No matter what our especial concern for a better future, whether it be natural beauty, adequate economic resources, sound social and political relations, our fundamental problem is one of design. We must view it in a total perspective, drawing upon all of the talents at our command.

It follows then that we cannot be effective by concentrating on legislation and persuasion to preserve what we now have. If our strategy is to succeed, it must concern itself with many matters that lie outside the boundaries of wilderness itself. No segment of the continental landscape is a thing apart.

We have passed the time when a group could ignore all resources except the one it was organized to protect—birds, trees, game, or whatever. Practical experience, no less than scientific ecology, have shown us that the ecosystem is an organic whole. The fisherman, who wants nothing more than a chance to fill his creel at a nearby stream, once thought that hatcheries were the simple answer to his problem. He knows now that clean water is his problem. To get it he must put pressure on municipalities, industry, and farms whose wastes have ruined the majority of our streams.

I suspect that friends of the wilderness will gain valuable allies by their support of the movement to restore the beauty of the American landscape, both urban and rural. As recommended to the President, and by him to Congress, this includes the location of and views from highways, the preservation of wild areas, the better planning of residential development, together with more and better urban and suburban parks, screening or removal of unsightly areas, and encouragement of varied and interesting farm lands.

Well kept and prosperous family farms, such as those in eastern Pennsylvania—strikingly like those in Switzerland—are certainly more attractive than the vast and monotonous factories in the fields. But no one has yet come up with a sound plan to protect these smaller operations from the fate of the corner grocery store. We suffer today from the prevalent notion that whatever is profitable and technically possible, automatically becomes right.

Essential to a good life is the ability to see and understand one's surroundings. Too many of us go through our journey half blind, despite good vision. With this defect, no one is likely to take much interest in local action, where so much good conservation must begin. Training in honest observation, I am convinced, must begin with the learning of mother-tongue and later training in communication. The present activity in improving science education at all levels is most encouraging, and will, I am certain, consider natural resources.

Yet, I look forward to the time when courses in conservation will no longer be needed. There is certainly an opportunity to deal with this problem in connection with most subjects now in the curriculum. I cannot conceive of teaching history without explaining the often decisive role of natural resources. Physics and chemistry, dealing as they do with matter and energy, have a fundamental relation to conservation. The role of sciences dealing directly with the earth and its life is obvious. So too, I may add, is that of the fine arts and humane letters, whose very stuff is intertwined with values.

I would hope that a new generation, imbued with the kind of experience I suggest, would see its connection with active political life and contribute some of its best individuals to it.

Without vision the people perish. In closing, I refer again to that great apostle of conservation, Samuel Perkins Marsh. Here are his words:

... next to moral and religious doctrine, I know no more important practical lessons in this earthly life of ours—which, to the wise man, is a school from the cradle to the grave—than those relating to the employment of the sense of vision in the study of nature.

THE IMPACT OF RECENT LEGISLATION ON ADMINISTRATIVE AGENCIES

➢➢ *Edward P. Cliff, Edward C. Crafts, George Hartzog, Jr., Charles H. Stoddard*

MR. EDWARD P. CLIFF: I am pleased to have this opportunity to talk with you again about the wilderness plans of the Forest Service. When I spoke to you in March, 1963, my remarks were directed to several reclassification actions and to the problems of maintaining high standards in designating Wilderness Areas. I also talked about the growing need for purposeful management of wilderness visitors so essential to protect the wilderness environment. Today it seems logical that I should discuss briefly the implementation of the wilderness legislation enacted last year as it relates to the national forests.

The Wilderness Act of 1964 culminates more than eight years of Congressional deliberation and public hearings. I congratulate you and the people you represent for the vital role you played throughout this long struggle. For the most part, the Wilderness Act confirms and endorses the wilderness concept pioneered by the Forest Service. Although the bulk of our policies and management practices remain unaltered by this new legislation, we have much work to do to implement it on the national forests.

As a result of the Act we must now prepare and publish new regulations, mostly procedural details to conform to requirements of the law. We must develop policies and instructions to guide our field people with regard to changes in administrative practices prescribed by the law. We must submit a map and legal description of each unit to Congress before September 3, 1965. Our biggest job is to study and report on the remaining 34 National Forest Primitive Areas. Of course, this is a continuation of the same general kind of work we were doing prior to the passage of the Act. We also have a host of other things to accomplish in connection with wilderness. For example, public interest generated by the law requires us to produce infor-national material for visitors and others. We also plan to pursue a strong program of basic and applied research in the ecology and management of wilderness. We must not only *do* more, we must also *know* more about wilderness, its use, and its management.

A tentative draft of the policy section of our wilderness manual will be available for review by interested parties before long. These national policies will of necessity be broad. The wide variation among wilderness units precludes any single set of rigid rules or procedures that our people could apply effectively on a Service-wide basis. Probably none could be devised to cover all situations in all places. Most of these differences are natural, but some result from the activities of man or from historic attitudes and uses. Consequently, uses which are accepted and management practices which are necessary on one national forest wilderness are frequently unnecessary or even unacceptable on others. So we have concluded that we must rely on relatively broad principles or policies to guide the preparation of specific management plans, plans that are custom tailored to fit the requirements and characteristics of each wilderness.

We believe that the wilderness which is managed best is managed least. By that I mean we intend to manipulate or change the environment as little as possible and to regulate visitor or user activities as unobtrusively as we possibly can—and then only as necessary.

We recognize both climax and successional biotic communities as natural and desirable in wilderness. Generally, we plan to permit ecological changes to occur naturally. However, positive management actions will be required in some situations to influence the composition and the condition of natural plant and animal associations. For example, we may need to offset adverse effects of man's influences in the past in order to restore natural conditions. Rare or endangered wildlife species may require special assistance to survive. Fire and insect and disease outbreaks will be controlled as necessary to prevent unacceptable losses of wilderness values or the spread of these destructive elements to adjoining land. Soil erosion caused by the activities of man may need to be controlled or prevented by reseeding native grasses or other species.

Actions which might influence natural ecological processes will be approved on a case by case basis and only when clearly justified by an appraisal of the situation or as required by the Act. To the extent possible, the actions themselves will be modified so that they will produce a minimum impact on the wilderness environment. Obviously, time does not permit me to discuss in detail our responses to the wide variety of situations where such actions may be indicated.

Certain non-wilderness uses are authorized under the new legislation. Although wilderness values are specified to be "dominant," we face some knotty problems in regulating nonconforming uses equitably within the full intent of the law. We anticipate that some of our most difficult administrative problems will arise in connection with mineral prospecting and mining.

The Secretary of Agriculture is required to issue reasonable regulations to permit mineral prospecting in a manner compatible with the preservation of the wilderness environment. Such regulations must also cover various activities on areas prospected and located, and on adjacent areas. There must be requirements for the restoration of surface areas disturbed in prospecting, development, and production. These regulations must effectively control mining activities as needed to maintain the wilderness environment to the fullest extent feasible. But, and here is where we might have difficulty, the law tells us these regulations must not block legitimate mining activity or become unreasonable obstructions.

One illustration of why each case must be decided on its merits relates to the mode of transportation used in prospecting, in transporting equipment, or otherwise. Obviously, we cannot permit widespread use of helicopters or jeeps or scooters or other mechanized equipment and still maintain anything remotely resembling a wilderness environment. Except in the most unusual circumstances, we must insist on the use of primitive means of transportation in ordinary wilderness prospecting, as we have done in the past. On the other hand, if heavy equipment is required to explore areas of high mineral potential, we would want to consider the most feasible and least destructive means of permitting its use. For example, helicopter transportation could be more desirable than construction of the temporary road that might otherwise be required. Our basic guideline seems clear. We should choose a mode of transportation that will cause the least permanent disturbance to wilderness values within each particular set of circumstances.

Keep in mind, too, that there are certain restrictions in mining, and in the Wilderness Act, and one of the important ones is that the mining law becomes ineffective as to new claims after 19 years. Nineteen years after passage of the Wilderness Act, this legislation separates surface rights from sub-surface rights. The mining locator would no longer acquire the surface rights of a valid mining claim that goes to patent, and that is an important departure.

The new Wilderness Act authorizes the Secretary to require restoration of disturbed areas, and this is a new authority. But these new authorities do not apply to valid mining claims that were filed prior to the passage of the Act—and there are several thousand of those in the Wilderness Areas—nor does it apply to mining and prospecting in the National Forest Primitive Areas. So we have another set of different kinds of problems under those circumstances.

The Wilderness Act makes it much more difficult to reduce or eliminate a classified Wilderness Area, as those of us who supported the passage of the Act wanted. However, we must face the fact that as proposals for addition to the Wilderness System go forward, they will also be carefully scrutinized, and there will be opposition from the same people who were opposed to the passage of the Wilderness Bill.

In addition to mining, the Act permits certain other nonconforming uses, facilities, and practices, and it recognizes existing private rights. It also provides for management practices and facilities necessary to meet minimum requirements for administration of wilderness. Except for these, our general policy will be to permit no roads, motorized equipment, structures, or landing of aircraft in wilderness. In applying this policy, we propose to take a rather hard-nosed attitude with respect to facilities and equipment. Our employees will be expected to use tents, travel on foot or horseback, and otherwise perform their duties under primitive conditions unless there are compelling reasons to the contrary. We expect other agencies and individuals to conform to these same practices in Wilderness and Primitive Areas.

We expect our people to be sensitive to wilderness values in managing lands in close proximity to units of the National Wilderness Preservation System. We will administer adjacent national forest lands on the basis of appropriate multiple-use plans. However, buffer strips of undeveloped wildland will not be maintained as informal extensions of the wilderness.

I hope this bird's-eye view has not raised more questions than it has answered. If it has, the draft policy statement is much more complete. I commend it to your attention when it becomes available.

I would like to say a few words about the ten-year job that lies ahead of us in reviewing and reclassifying each of the National Forest Primitive Areas. The law requires that we report on not less than $\frac{1}{3}$ of the 34 areas within three years and on at least $\frac{2}{3}$ within seven years. Obviously, this is a large, top priority job. We gave a list of areas to the Geological Survey and the Bureau of Mines. They have studied the maps, reviewed the information they now have available, and have given us a list showing the probable sequence in which they can get their part of the job done. The two lists do not coincide at all. In some of the areas on which we want to move quickly, they indicate that it will take considerable time for them to accomplish their mission; so we have a job of reconciling this problem.

We must face the fact that the Wilderness Act made the establishment of additional Wilderness much more difficult. Before the Act, the Secretary of Agriculture could establish a Wilderness Area with a stroke of the pen, and I could do the same for Wild Areas without some of the procedural requirements we now must go through. In contrast, the law now requires that other Federal agencies, governors, county officials, and interested individuals be invited to comment. A public hearing *must* be held in each state in which the Wilderness occurs. All views submitted must be made a part of the report to the Secretary, the President, and the Congress. We anticipate that this will be a time-consuming process. And as you know, all actions to reclassify Primitive Areas or to create new Wilderness require affirmative action by the Congress. This will involve preparation of legislation, making legislative reports, and participating in congressional hearings. This is part of the price that all of us were willing to pay to gain statutory recognition and protection of wilderness.

I hope that advocates of quick action on certain of these 34 Primitive Areas and potential new Wilderness Areas will be reasonably patient and understanding of the problems involved. Many factors influence the sequence in which we will be able to consider them. For example, as I pointed out, Congress has made it clear that it expects a study and report on mineralization by the Geological Survey and the Bureau of Mines in each case. The sequence in which this can be accomplished may not necessarily coincide with the priorities which you, or we, would like to follow.

We have set an objective for ourselves to complete our report on each of the 34 Primitive Areas within seven years. I hope we can make it!

In the past we identified as potential wilderness those areas which seemed predominantly valuable and needed for that purpose. We will continue to do this as time and funds permit.

In the Forest Service, we know that in implementing our part of this new legislation, we have embarked on a big job with far-reaching implications. It will tax our organization to the utmost to accomplish what is expected of us in the allotted time. Obviously we need and welcome all the help and support from you that you can bring to bear. Perhaps in one of your future conferences we can look back together on an era of solid accomplishments in adding to and managing the National Wilderness Preservation System. I sincerely hope so.

* * * * *

MR. EDWARD C. CRAFTS: From what I have read in the papers about hydroelectric dams and the growth of the Sierra Club, I can only conclude that Parkinson's Law applies not only to bureaucracy, but to our whole population, and I think it applies particularly to the Sierra Club. I congratulate you on it.

Your program places me between the Forest Service and the National Park Service. I found myself in a similar situation in Washington State recently at another gathering. This is not an unfamiliar position. I cite you the proposed Oregon Dunes National Seashore and the North Cascades where there has been a storm brewing for some time. I cite you the question of the utilization of the Land and Water Conservation Fund Act moneys, between the Forest Service, the National Park Service, and the Bureau of Fish and Wildlife—and particularly the instructions we received from the House of Representatives in a review and proposal for Federal acquisitions. We are in the middle.

I have often been asked what it is like to be on the other side. What people mean is, what is it like to be in the Department of the Interior after I have been in the Department of Agriculture so long. I know what they mean, but I cannot accept the premise which lies behind the question.

If you do nothing else as a result of this conference, I hope that you take the time to read and digest the President's Message on Natural Beauty. The President tested the natural beauty waters in Ann Arbor last June. He tested them again in Portland last fall. The Message on Natural Beauty, delivered in February [1965], is a charter for the future in conservation. It is creative thinking at its best.

This new climate for conservation and recreation, and the Bureau of Outdoor Recreation's role in it, deserve our attention.

I think the President called for the turn last September 3, when he signed both the Wilderness Act and the Land and Water Conservation Fund Act at the same time in the White House rose garden. He referred to the first two great leaders in conservation: first, Theodore Roosevelt, a great Republican President, who established the concept of Federal stewardship; and later, Franklin D. Roosevelt, a great Democratic President, who established the TVA, the CCC, and the Soil Conservation Service, among many other accomplishments in this period.

The third great period of conservation leadership, I think, is now. The 88th Congress has often been cited as the greatest conservation Congress in history. Some 30 conservation acts were passed by that Congress. You know about the Wilderness Act, and you have at least heard about the Land and Water Conservation Fund Act.

Others in which this group has a particular interest would include the statutes authorizing establishment of Canyonlands National Park, Fire Island National Seashore, Ozark National Scenic Riverways, Lake Mead National Recreation Area—the first national recreation area created by an Act of Congress—and the Organic Act for the Bureau of Outdoor Recreation, which specifically mentions Wilderness Areas in its reference to Forest Service acquisitions.

Under that Act, we are commissioned to prepare an overall Nationwide Outdoor Recreation Plan which must be submitted to Congress by 1968. This encompassed the activities of the private sector, the municipalities, the states, and the Federal Government, and the various phases of outdoor recreation, including wilderness.

The Organic Act of the Bureau of Outdoor Recreation directs that the Federal agencies carry out their outdoor recreation programs in general conformance with the Bureau's nationwide plan.

The states must prepare statewide recreation plans in order to participate in the Land and Water Conservation Fund. These plans must consider not only state, local, and private activities, but must take cognizance of the Federal activity in outdoor recreation in the respective states.

Under the Organic Act there is the directive to promote coordination of Federal activities in this general field. I think our activities in the North Cascades are a good example: depending on which we come out with there, decisions may be made by the cabinet officers, or other decisions may be made by Congress. In the last analysis, the decisions will be made by you people sitting here—and others like you.

Now, a little bit more about the Land and Water Conservation Fund Act; it is fairly simple and basic.

It does two things. It sets up a fund and provides a guide for the use of the fund.

The moneys in the fund come from the sale of surplus Federal real estate, from motor boat fuel tax, from user fees, from entrance fees to designated Federal recreation areas, and from the Recreation-Conservation Sticker. The sticker is one way to implement the entrance fee provisions of the Act.

The Fund has a 25-year life. It is estimated that $125 million a year will go into the Fund, for a period of 25 years . . . and added to that are the matching funds which the states must contribute. You can see that the potential here is for substantial moneys to further the planning, acquisition, and development of outdoor recreation facilities. These moneys, if appropriated by the Congress and the states, run into several billion.

Concerning the use of the Fund, roughly 40 percent of these moneys will go to the Federal agencies, for acquisition primarily by three agencies—the Forest Service, the National Park Service, and the Bureau of Sports Fisheries. Utilization of funds for wilderness purposes is specifically named in the Act so far as the Forest Service is concerned.

About 60 percent will go to the state agencies. The Appropriations Committee recognized the philosophy of the Act by fully funding it. The House of Representatives has already passed the Appropriations Bill, which approved $125 million for the Fund in the coming fiscal year. The House made some adjustments between Federal and state sharing and between Federal and state participation.

One other thing. The Secretary, in the administration of the Act, has been directed to give primary emphasis to serving the needs of urban populations. I think there is no question that most of the people who use the wilderness, as well as most of the people who love the wilderness—but never use it—live in the cities.

Also, perhaps you do not realize that of the 14 million acres of National Forest Wilderness and Primitive Areas, some two and a quarter million acres are located in, or close to, the standard metropolitan statistical areas of the Bureau of Census. So the Wilderness Areas are not always in the hinterlands, as many people believe.

I might say also that the acquisition or development of recreation areas by states or local governments under the Fund Act will tend to have an indirect rather than direct effect on Wilderness Areas and wilderness lovers. This is because such recreation areas and facilities will certainly tend to relieve the overload which otherwise would plague and perhaps ruin some of the best wilderness.

Also, such state or local areas may provide recreation opportunities for the many people who want wilderness but don't like too much wilderness—people who like a little convenience along with the undeveloped areas.

As the Act went through Congress, admission fees cannot be charged for entrance to Wilderness Areas. Basically, I think this is wrong. I don't see why the users of the wilderness should not pay; however, those who did not want to pay were successful, and wilderness is the only specific recreation use that is so exempt.

I want to say a few words about one piece of pending legislation that Senator Anderson mentioned—the Wild Rivers proposal. The Wild Rivers Bill was introduced in the Congress with 29 senators co-sponsoring it. Wild Rivers are not necessarily wilderness rivers, and the proposal first is to establish segments of six rivers as Wild Rivers, and to study nine additional rivers. There are no rivers in California in this group. I think there should be.

This bill has rough sailing ahead. There are powerful interests that oppose the provisions of the Wild Rivers Bill. But the Wilderness Act took some time to come into being, and this Act may also take some time to come into being. When it does, however, in my judgment it will be a fitting sequel to the Wilderness Act.

There are other proposals: for a national system of scenic roads and parkways; for a national system of trails; for some 12 new recreation areas, mentioned in the President's Natural Beauty Message; the legislation to protect endangered species; a survey of surplus military lands for their conservation values. . . . And this is all going to be wrapped up, in a sense, in a White House Conference this coming May. One of the features of this conference will be the first public meeting of the President's Recreation Advisory Council.

The success of this whole program hinges in large measure on the sale of the Recreation-Conservation Sticker. We are hopeful that as much as a third of the funding under the Act will come from sticker sales and other entrance, admission, and user fees. I know that if the recreationists are not willing to pay through the purchase of the sticker, Congress won't legislate, and Congress won't appropriate. It is up to you.

I want to say that the Sierra Club has been the greatest single individual purchaser of stickers to date. I have seen a check for 50 stickers from the Sierra Club and I was immensely pleased. Prior to that, Laurance Rockefeller and myself had each bought 10 stickers—the largest sale, up to that time. This is the only time in my life I will ever be equated financially with Rockefeller.

Don't be complacent just because the Wilderness Act has passed. Ride the tide; take advantage of the fact that you have a responsive official and executive branch at the present time. You also have responsive members in Congress. It is not too frequently that this combination exists. Above all, I hope the Sierra Club never loses its militancy. If you become complacent, your value is gone. We have begun. Let us carry on. And remember, it is not we bureaucrats who do it; it is the hot breath of public opinion.

*   *   *   *   *

GEORGE HARTZOG, JR.: We live in a country young in years and, I hope, young in heart! Never is this fact more clearly recognized than when we look back to the legendary figures of our past and find that we Americans have no ancient history.

Jim Bridger was one of the great figures of our wilderness history. He was born in 1804, the year Lewis and Clark set out on their epic voyage of discovery, and during his lifetime he was witness to the passing of the frontiers of the explorer, the fur trader, the miner, the Indian fighter, and the cattleman. There are many men now living who were alive in 1881, the year Jim Bridger died. And so, in the short span of two lifetimes, we can go back in our history to the administration of Thomas Jefferson.

Every American who has lived out his allotted three score years and ten, has seen the face and the character of his country undergo an enormous change. Television and penicillin, the jet plane and the atomic bomb, and the fantastic developments of the space age—these are the revolutions of our lifetimes.

For more than 70 years—the years of greatest change in the face of America—the Sierra Club has devoted its energies to the cause of protecting the natural beauty of this country. Your motto has been "not blind opposition to progress, but opposition to blind progress."

This is a way of saying that progress cannot be made at the expense of the future generation. It was this concept which Secretary Udall advanced so eloquently in his book, *The Quiet Crisis,* when he said: "Each generation has its own rendezvous with the land."

If we are to keep our own appointed rendezvous with the land of our fathers, we must do so with our own plan of conservation, and not the plan of our fathers.

President Johnson has challenged us to develop a new conservation, and in his recent message on Natural Beauty, he said:

> To deal with these new problems will require a new conservation. We must not only protect the countryside and save it from destruction, we must restore what has been destroyed and salvage the beauty and charm of our cities. Our conservation must be not just a classic conservation of protection and development, but a creative conservation of restoration and innovation. Its concern is not with nature alone but with the total relation between man and the world around him . . .

This philosophy, to me, admirably translates the contributions of the past into the needs of the present. Yosemite was not as desperately needed in 1864 as it was in 1964; the protection of this great park for a century now grants to us the opportunity to make use of new techniques of park management in such a way that our needs might be fulfilled without jeopardizing the needs of our children.

True, the predictions of park use for 1975 and 1985 would seem to indicate the parks will be overwhelmed, the wilderness tramped into oblivion. But these same predictions have been made periodically in the past, and I do not believe that park resources have yet been depleted.

I happen to be one that firmly believes the wilderness lands of this nation will be endangered more by the restrictive and inflexible concepts of park managers than they will be by the expanding use of park visitors.

Time is a great healer, particularly of the unpleasant episodes of the past, and the "good old days" which many of us remember do not survive the impartial view of the historian.

Do you remember when campsites and hotels occupied the most beautiful sites in the park, and public accommodations were built without regard to architectural or landscape or scientific values?

Do you remember when roadsides were burned to preserve the view, when a colony of summer homes intruded upon the Giant Forest, when predators were hunted down and killed, and when 20,000 sheep were driven out of Yosemite in one year?

Wilderness had yet to be singled out as a resource to be either reserved or managed for the contributions and values it might make to our way of life. The need had not yet arisen.

Congressional concern with wilderness is a comparatively recent development. The Yellowstone legislation made no mention of wilderness nor did the National Park Service Act of 1916.

The measures that had been taken in the national parks to retain natural features and scenic resources in their natural condition were primarily intended for the people's recreation and enjoyment, and they were sufficient for the times. The concept served well to preserve as a side benefit the very real wilderness that was included in them and that would, in our day, become a focal point for our management.

Seventy years ago the famous wilderness back country of Sequoia and Kings Canyon national parks was perilously close to permanent destruction. So thoroughly had sheep done their work that the once lush alpine meadows and grasslands were dusty flats. Eroded gullies were everywhere. Much of the climax vegetation was gone, and the High Sierra was virtually impassable to stock parties due to scarcity of feed. In 1893, the Acting Superintendent of Sequoia National Park recommended that cavalry be replaced by infantry. No natural forage was available for horses.

Today, under National Park Service management policies, Sequoia and Kings Canyon national parks contain wilderness to compare with any other national park. And, in spite of increasing public use in the back country, these areas are in a better condition today than they were 70 years ago.

The natural resources of the Great Smoky Mountains, too, had suffered from misuse, having been settled for more than a hundred years when the National Park was authorized in 1926. The Blue Ridge Mountains of the Shenandoah National Park were once described as the most abused mountains in the world. Today, nearly 40 years later, the restorative processes of nature have once again clothed these areas in native forest mantle. Today's traveler to these parks sees little evidence of their harsh past. Tomorrow's visitor will have a keen reminder of the unbelievably rich and varied eastern hardwood forests that once stood as a wilderness barrier to the seaboard colonists.

We believe that, in view of the past history of the Great Smokies, the introduction of one-way motor trails which ease the congestion of the single cross-park highway and help visitors experience the back country beauty, is an innovation of the kind President Johnson has called for.

The passage of the Wilderness Act last year was evidence both of congressional concern and of the paramount importance of wilderness today. With this decisive new directive from the Congress, we must begin to look at what we have in the way of wilderness and what it portends in the area of land management and visitor use.

Our distinguished Under Secretary at noon will discuss some of the wilderness preservation procedures and regulations that are being promulgated by the Department. Suffice for me to say that we expect to examine the wilderness as a part of our master planning practice. We expect in our master planning practice not only to deal with those areas which are to be developed and devoted to public use, as we have historically in the past, but we expect also to define those areas which will not be developed. We expect also, as does the Forest Service and others managing areas subject to the Wilderness Act, to hold public hearings on the proposals that we make with regard to the wilderness boundaries in the National Park System. These hearings we plan to have conducted by a single hearing examiner, rather than augmenting or establishing any special organization for the handling of this program.

Wilderness and natural places cannot be preserved by simply drawing a boundary around them and letting them alone. The magnificent wilderness of the Yellowstone has been threatened by over-population of wildlife more than by visitor use of back-country trails. The elk, a native species, are restricted to ranges within the park by adverse influences and conditions outside. For years their numbers have far exceeded the capacity of the range to meet their food requirements. Not only are native grasses, shrubs, and even trees threatened with depletion, but also other native wildlife species such as buffalo, mountain sheep, antelope, and deer are exposed to competition which poses serious questions regarding their future.

Our responsibilities for wilderness management are strengthened and heightened under the Wilderness Act. We are cognizant that more than ever we must evolve new and dynamic concepts of management to attain the goals that have been laid down.

We subscribe to the policy that wilderness management should be achieved with a minimum of controls and restrictions on use, as they tend to limit the very freedom through which a wilderness experience becomes meaningful. Nevertheless, we recognize that conditions may necessitate some regulation of use in the wilderness areas of national parks so that the freedom which contributes to *enjoyment* of nature does not ultimately lead to the *defeat* of nature.

We anticipate the need to augment our staffs of back-country rangers and naturalists so that we can manage adequately the wilderness resources of the national parks as more and more people use them. The back-country ranger must come to be as much a public contact man as he is an enforcer. How wonderful it would be if the back-country traveler could count upon meeting one of these uniformed men on the trail or visit with them over a campfire, and receive the same personal welcome to the park that is now extended visitors at the roads.

We are also confident that wilderness management requires special skills and special attention that can only be attained through specially qualified personnel. Expertise of this kind is needed *now* as we consider programs designed to introduce the public to wilderness.

We intend to experiment further with the concept of the wilderness threshold. The wilderness threshold implies both a physical location and a kind of experience. It can serve not only as a buffer for the primitive wilderness but also as a zone of orientation where the newcomer may explore the mood and temper of the wild country beyond that beckons him, if he is prepared and willing to use it on its own terms. The wilderness threshold provides unequalled opportunity for interpretation of the meaning of wilderness. We are vitally interested in devising methods, techniques, and programs that will impart understanding and appreciation of wilderness.

I am not thinking solely of the wilderness threshold as a place on the edge of wilderness. I am talking about bringing the experience of the wilderness threshold into the environment of our cities.

John Muir once said: "When we try to pick out something by itself, we find it hitched to everything else in the universe."

We find his wisdom helpful today as we consider together the management of wilderness and the needs of burgeoning city populations. You in the Sierra Club love the back country and are willing and able to use it on its own terms. But the great preponderance of our citizens living today in urban environments may never see wilderness or have the opportunity to experience the tingling excitement of hiking mountain trails, in solitude, hand in hand with God. Yet, it is important, I believe, that we offer them an opportunity to experience something of the pleasures of solitude in natural areas close at hand—a pleasure not unlike that which you have experienced in the wilderness or that which one may experience driving along a narrow, tree-lined parkway when you feel more remote than you really are.

Citizens who have respect for our land and for nature and its ways have gained much satisfaction from their association with wilderness and have done much to preserve it for all of us. These same people can now help us in preserving parks and open space in our cities and in so doing will indirectly contribute to the preservation of real wilderness.

Just ten years ago, Dave Brower and representatives of a number of other nationally respected conservation organizations came to Washington, D.C., to testify before the Senate Committee on Interior and Insular Affairs. The point at issue then was not a great national park with its expanse of wilderness. Rather it was the issue of whether an expressway should be driven lengthwise through the heart of Rock Creek Park. Dave and the others provided as thoughtful a statement of the values of Rock Creek Park as I have yet seen. As you recall, the freeway idea was thrown out. But the point I want to make is this—that the eloquent defense of this city park was made by men who know and love the wilderness. As one reads through their testimony, it is unmistakably clear that they were talking about *wilderness* values and *wilderness* experiences.

The task now is not solely to keep freeways out of parks. It is the less tangible but equally vital fight to put beauty and quiet and nature into our cities where most of us spend most of our time.

The American conservation movement has reached another milestone comparable to the Homestead Act and the Yellowstone Act. The Wilderness Act indicates that we are still adjusting to the changing needs of our nation.

We can be proud of our conservation heritage. We are entering a new phase of this movement, and we can look forward with a degree of satisfaction. We can also be assured that there is still plenty of room in this work for ingenuity, skill, dedication, and—most of all—a love for our common cause.

*   *   *   *   *

CHARLES H. STODDARD: The Bureau of Land Management, U.S. Department of the Interior, administers approximately 460 million acres of public domain lands, including some 280 million acres in Alaska. This huge residue is about a fifth of the whole land area of the United States.

These lands have a wide variety of uses and values, including recreation and space in which to roam. Until now it has not been possible for the Bureau to make long-term plans for the management of these lands. Over the years an ideological debate has been raging between custodianship and management.

But now new legislation has been enacted—the Public Land Law Review Commission and the Public Sales Act—which bring the whole process of land disposal to a turning point in our history. The Public Land Law Review Commission was designed to review the land laws of the 50 states and to bring them in line with the modern requirements of our nation. For the first time we have a clear directive for multiple-use management of the retained land and a clear directive for disposal of those lands which are more suitable to other uses than to Federal management.

We have a great responsibility in exercising the authority of these two acts, because for the first time we are charged with developing a set of criteria which can be applied to classification of these lands for retention in long-term multiple-use management or for disposal under systematic procedures.

We are in the process of holding hearings on the regulations for these classifications. These hearings—one of which has been held in Washington, four of which will be held in the field—are based on the concept of consultation with the people in the areas affected. While these lands belong to all the people, they have an especially strong impact in areas where large acreages of public domain lands affect the local economies. Therefore, our planning based on these regulations must be comprehensive.

Our initial plans in the 12 western states show roughly 11 million acres suitable for disposal to a variety of local needs—commercial, industrial, and residential, as well as parking space. And we have a requirement by law saying we must have a plan and a zoning system set up in the area before these lands may be turned over for non-Federal ownership. This is having quite an electric effect on planning in areas where there has been none before. We now have the responsibility for developing long-range multiple-use management plans on roughly 150 million acres, with the final decision, of course, being based on local hearings.

Recently we have undertaken several other activities in which you will be particularly interested. We have made a careful review of the potential natural areas on public lands in a variety of situations—situations where we have pre-historic and archaeological remains or where we have certain combinations of vegetation which are all too rare. We have identified nearly a hundred of these relatively small tracts, some of which have been put on protective withdrawal, and these areas now will be examined over the next several years to determine how they may be used for scientific purposes.

We also have a means of identifying those parts of the public lands which may have some wilderness potential, recognizing that we have a lot of open desert, a lot of open mountain top, and a great deal of grassland. We also have much forest land and tundra in Alaska.

These lands represent probably the last potential additions to the Wilderness System, and the Multiple Use and Classification Act gives authority for the identification and designation of these areas under a systematic procedure. We have asked Sierra Club members and other conservation groups living in these areas to call them to the attention of our field people so that they can be examined in more detail.

Briefly, this is a direction we are heading in the administration of the remaining public domain lands. We are using the concept of zoning to prescribe appropriate land and water uses. We feel that it is possible to have planned development in some areas and planned preservation in others—that they can exist side by side. If we can accomplish this goal, we will demonstrate that we can learn from the mistakes of the past by the best knowledge of the present and solve the problems in the future which we will certainly face.

WILDERNESS—
THE CITIZEN'S EVALUATION

≫ Albert Lepawsky

Five years ago the *Sierra Club Bulletin* lamented the profligate "alteration of the American landscape" and deplored the fact that during the 1960 Presidential campaign "neither party evinced awareness of the magnitude of the profligacy." In the last couple of years this famine in American resources policy has become a feast of Federal action and enactment: a long-range wilderness policy; a national recreation program under the U.S. Bureau of Outdoor Recreation; a comprehensive review of public land laws; a ten-year development program under a Cabinet-level council to sponsor regional river-basin planning commissions which will coordinate Federal with state and local conservation of water and related resources; the earmarking of funds and facilities for systematic and scientific water research; the beginnings of pollution and pesticide control; re-planning our regional and national grid of energy resources; continued tightening up of our mineral conservation laws; continued experimentation with the rehabilitation of our urban environment; financial assistance for the acquisition of green belts; encouragement of experimental new towns; the beginnings of metropolitan reorganization; and even the calling of a White House Conference on Natural Beauty.

There had been earlier highpoints of achievement in American resources policy and administration. In the 1860s, for example, a confluence of national forces during the crisis of Civil War produced the Homestead Act as a belated measure of land tenure reform and the Morrill Act for the development of our agricultural and resource sciences and technologies—and of our other intellectual disciplines as well—at our newly burgeoning state universities. Again by 1910, we were able to give a twentieth century lift to our forest reservation and our other preservation policies by launching on the American

180]

scene the conservation and rural life movements, this time through Presidential leadership and without benefit of Congress—in fact, with some congressional hostility. But now, in the second decade of the second half of the twentieth century, that the President and Congress both should undertake a bi-partisan, inter-sectional campaign to restore a wide range of our ravaged natural resources and blighted regions—and to do this at the very time our international and national problems seem to be overwhelming us and our industrial-urban complex is displacing the historic agrarianism that has dominated our power structure—this is one of the grand paradoxes of American political history.

To the hardy conservationists and others with outdoor interests here assembled in the Ninth Biennial Wilderness Conference, this fortunate turn in our national policy-making is not so paradoxical. Our explanation is the obvious one: Homus Americanus has finally awakened just in time to the fact that in blighting his natural habitat, he has almost destroyed himself; and by this timely revival of the conservation movement he is preserving his bio-psychic integrity against the inroads of industrialization, mechanization, computerization, urbanization, metropolitanization, even suburbanization—that false image of the natural way of life.

American conservationists today take special pride in the fact that the political pressure now favoring primitivism is no longer dependent on the Thoreauean aristocrats of the Atlantic seaboard, keen on preserving their family retreats along the Appalachian trail. Gone is the day of those blue-blooded conservationists of American history and their staunch eastern congressmen upon whom the nation depended for the defense not only of the Appalachians, but also the Ozarks, the Rockies, and the Sierra. For once, a New England President and his Texan successor in the White House, backed by a more tractable Congress, has been able to persevere, thanks to the widespread support of East and West, Republican and Democrat, white-collared professional and blue-shirted technician, city and country. If this analysis holds water, it would seem that when we meet in our Tenth Biennial Conference in 1967, on the eve of the 1968 election, both political parties will have their scouts scattered through our audience—and not limited to this talented rostrum—taking notes on how best to bid for the wilderness vote, which by then may constitute the leading political coalition in the country, bigger than the Farm Bloc, the Labor Vote, Big Business, and the Civil Rights Movement.

My very overstatement of this Utopian eventuality betrays my skepticism that it will actually come to pass. Rather, I fear that the Good Ship Conservation faces many shoals ahead. Indeed, we wilderness enthusiasts ought to ponder the possibility that we are at the apex, not the upsurge, of our power.

Let us look first at our situation in terms of existing natural resources policy. The primary historic American policy here has been that of sustaining the physical yield of our resource base, especially by means of governmentally provided supervision, support, subsidy, and science.

We continue to make remarkable progress in the sustained yield of natural resources, but sheer productivity brings in its wake serious problems of economic, ecologic, and environmental imbalance. With specific reference to the supply of wildlife or recreation areas, there is increasingly severe competition from uses of resources for urbanization and housing, industrial development and transportation rights-of-way, military and space installations, education and research institutions, and other consumptive uses of our remaining spaces and sites. Realistically speaking, that two percent figure we insist upon for wilderness or primitive areas may never be attained and certainly will not be exceeded, although our future recreational and greenbelt spaces may be more readily forthcoming. We may actually have to bargain away our primitive for our cultivated recreational resources. After all, how much of a wilderness area can we "use" and still retain its wild character? There is actually very little land completely untrammeled by man. What we want to insure is that primitive areas will be preserved and will be experienced in moderation. Perhaps we need, on the French model, more flexible and experimental sites for both recreational and wildlife purposes, with concentric zones of descending uses, from open parks to completely virgin core areas that may be observed but not trodden.

This brings us to experimentation, research, and science in the realm of natural resources, which has, over the years, been a second basic resource policy in this country. We are still the envy of the world in respect to resources research and training. However, research into the resources of outer space consumes an increasing share of our budget. Until proven to the contrary, we might well assume there will be some spillover for our earthbound resource sciences as a result of our strategic forays into space. Yet, space research is and will continue to be a diversion. Moreover, even our basic and applied researches into conventional resources—materials and energies, waters and lands, spaces and amenities—are also very expensive, and genuinely relevant education and training in resources management remains hard to attain and costly to achieve. Certainly recreational research and the science of wildlife management will be one of the luxuries we will expand last and curtail first as we face continuing budgetary pressures.

Thirdly there is the related American resources policy of the multiple management of resources. In this respect, recreationists as well as wildlife conservationists have special cause to be grateful. Had there been no vast multipurpose resource projects combining flood control, forestry, irrigation, power, and other functions, recreational development might have lagged still farther behind. Recent decisions, by which recreation has been recognized as a financial feasibility factor to be written into cost-and-benefit formulae for multipurpose public works, offer an invaluable stimulus to amenity resource planning and administration. Admittedly, the more comprehensive kind of resources planning prevalent some 25 years ago under the National Resources Planning Board is now lacking. And despite somewhat better sectorial planning even in a field like recreation administration, we have a long way to go before we establish effective partnership in resources policy and administration among our Federal, state, local, and private interests and institutions.

It is precisely on this borderland between our private interests and our public concerns that we will find most of our future problems, and our hopes too, in the realm of recreation. Existing resources policies in this respect are only moderately relevant to wildlife. Yet we would do well to study some of these, such as our anti-speculation policy in the field of reclamation and our other efforts to sustain rural ways of life and resource-based ways of making a living in industrial America. Some of us conservationists are reputedly so non-political and selfless about our defense of nature that we run the risk of neglecting such mundane matters. Those who are more conscious of the other political interest-groups involved often think only in terms of the irresponsible exploiters and corporate whipping-boys of an earlier generation.

We should now, instead, begin to adjust ourselves to the newly up-thrusting groups in American society, economically deprived but politically powerful, who will soon be injecting themselves in unprecedented ways into the political economy of natural resources. I refer to those expectant millions in our society who are classified as poverty-stricken and those still seeking their unfulfilled political, as well as economic, rights. These two overlapping groups are now on the threshold of a new emancipation, thanks to our dynamic economy of abundance and our unrequited search for political democracy. Increasingly articulate, ably led, popularly supported by a rising public opinion in their favor, they are yet to be heard from on matters of natural resources and outdoor recreation. But once they get their well-deserved voting rights and taste the power of economic reform through massive governmental measures, it is unlikely that they are going to sit idly by during budget-making time or pork-barrel season when national subsidies are being doled out, or during policy-making sessions when the nation's resources are being reparceled. In the competitive struggle for power and policy, they are going to have some ideas, and some votes too, on resources policy, land administration, soils and spaces, waters and energies. Why should we assume that, in the struggle for appropriations and legislation, they will vote for our favorite conceptions of parks and primitive areas and seashores, instead of for their own more essential preferences and priorities?

So far, our most reliable studies show that the users of some of these recreational facilities possess two distinct characteristics: they rank in the upper half of the income scale, and they have more than an average education. It is quite possible that as we upgrade our population economically and educationally, we will accelerate the use of our recreation and wild lands; but then, too, we will have to appropriate more funds for these services. Above all, we must remember how sticky our unemployment problem remains in the heyday of our prosperity, how nip-and-tuck our automated economy is for millions of our fellow citizens, how pressed they are in their local governments and urban neighborhoods to maintain minimal housing and community services. Should we not expect them, at first at least, to prefer other resource policies than recreationism or primitivism? Their more immediate stake is in steady jobs, better neighborhoods, and more adequate public services as a stabler basis for family and community life. Those of us who presume to make resources policies in the public interest share some of the responsibility for looking out for their best interests, especially if they simultaneously serve our own.

We should, therefore, search diligently for such common ground. But our search will be unrewarded unless we adopt a more flexible point of view toward the role of nature in the daily lives of the average man, not only for vacationers and week-enders like ourselves. I will only make one suggestion in this connection and leave the rest for future discussion and consideration.

Resource-based ways of life—not only the badly battered family-size farm, but also other dispersed ways of making a living and patterns of living throughout the vast non-urban hinterland of this still comparatively sparsely settled country—will pay greater dividends in support of nature and wildlife and recreation, than any other single policy we conservationists can concoct. I admit we have so far been highly successful in concentrating, militantly and single-mindedly, on our one specific objective of preserving nature untrammeled, so to speak. But I would not be completely candid, if I did not point out that the time of the mono-policy of preservation is running out. If we really want to make progress in keeping man linked with nature, we must create new models of the old homestead, and we must seek new allies among men who are searching for qualitatively better ways of life. We must look for our natural allies among more of the common citizenry. We must prepare ourselves for, and also speed the time when, these newer groups and generations of urbanites and sub-urbanites will begin to ask themselves, and us, whether they have to continue in such overwhelming proportions the drift to the cities where they will continue to be at the constant mercy of technological or cyclical unemployment.

What new policies and programs in respect to resource use will we have ready when these people demand more of a share and a stake in the riches and resources of this country? In helping to answer this question, let us not continue to give the impression that we are more interested in plants and animals than we are in men and women searching for economic security and social stability. This is the point, and now is the time to start a tamer and more ordered consideration of our natural and wild resources.

FROM THE DISCUSSION

Edward P. Cliff, Edward C. Crafts, George Hartzog, Jr.,
Albert Lepawsky, Charles H. Stoddard
        ⋙ *William E. Siri, Chairman*

MODERATOR SIRI: The first question relates to the Land and Water Conservation Fund: "Is the 125 million dollar figure to be matched to give a total of 250 million dollars?"

MR. CRAFTS: No, not the 125 million dollars. That will be divided by Congress in the Appropriations Act; so much available to the Federal agencies and so much available to the states. The Administration recommended that it be divided, 75 million dollars available for states, and 50 million dollars to the Federal agencies. The 75 million dollars which would be available to the states, if Congress accepts this, would have to be matched by the states on the 40–60 ratio, so that they would have to put up 90 million dollars in addition.

MODERATOR SIRI: We now have a question directed to Mr. Cliff: "Can you cite an example of the manipulations in the management of forest land which you feel best meet your aims of minimal management but which still achieve your required goals?"

MR. CLIFF: I think there are a number of examples. One of the problems that plague us in the management of some of our Wilderness Areas is the matter of providing feed for pack and saddle horses. I know you, who have used some of these Wilderness Areas, have inquired about some of the conditions that have developed on some small mountain meadows and camping spots where there is concentration and overuse of the natural vegetation. In those kinds of situations we feel that we are going to have to give nature a chance to restore those areas, and we might even have to give a helping hand by reseeding with native plants. We might have to restrict the use of pack and saddle stock or require the hauling in of forage.

Another example is the encroachment of tree reproduction on natural meadows. There are some people that feel we should cut or otherwise destroy the young trees that are gradually filling in the openings which are so valuable for wildlife. From my viewpoint, we would have to be very very careful in interferring with the natural processes of nature in this regard. However, we have to balance that against the broad view of general maintenance of habitat for wildlife that depends on open spaces for their food supplies.

MODERATOR SIRI: I have a loaded question for Mr. Hartzog: "What do you think of the State Natural Resources Agency's proposal for a Redwood Parkway instead of a Redwood Park, as described in a recent newspaper article?"

MR. HARTZOG: We were just talking about that and we were prepared to make a comment on that Monday. But now that you asked the question, we have been talking with a great many people and a great many organizations about the proposal which we made in our professional report, financed by the National Geographic Society. Of course, we welcome all of these comments and proposals.

Dr. Crafts and I have been asked by the Secretary to prepare a draft of a report for his consideration. This report will be prepared after collaboration and discussion with the State and full consideration of all the proposals that have been made, including those that have been made by the American Forestry Association, which we are going to hear about on Monday. We have been talking with the industry, and we understand that they have some suggestions. We welcome those as we have welcomed the suggestions which have been received from the Sierra Club, Save-the-Redwoods League, and others.

We think it has merit; we are grateful for the interest the State has taken in this; we think they are a dynamic party in arriving at a final solution to the question of what needs to be done about saving the great Coast Redwoods.

MODERATOR SIRI: Here is a question for Mr. Cliff: "What are the possibilities of blocking mining-development roads to public use after the mining period to prevent public pressure for continuing their use?"

MR. CLIFF: There are a lot of unanswered questions about this matter of access. The Act itself is not very clear. It does say that there will be no unreasonable restrictions put in the way of mining. It has specific reference to access by the methods which are customary in similar areas.

I just had a heated discussion with an owner of some mining claims in one of our Wilderness Areas yesterday, and he says that his lawyer advises him that he is entitled to a road to get access to his mining property. Naturally, that would be considered the customary method to get to his property.

I don't believe that the public would be entitled to use those roads, but it is something I am not sure of. The law would authorize the Secretary of Agriculture to require the restoration of the disturbed surface and that would include roads. And if roads were no longer usable or no longer needed for the mining operation, I would interpret the law as meaning that we could require the miner to put that road back to nature as nearly as is feasible. In other words, reseed it, revegetate it, and make it so it is no longer a road.

MODERATOR SIRI: Here is a question for Professor Lepawsky: "How do you think we can present man's relation to nature so as to win allies among the poor and those in the civil rights ranks?"

PROFESSOR LEPAWSKY: My recommendation was the other way around: accept their ideas insofar as they desire to remain closer to nature in their way of life. By proper policies, support those who desire to remain on so-called uneconomic family farms, to hunt squirrels in the Appalachians, to stay away from computorized jobs in the city, to live in the countryside and work in resource-based enterprises, to live in the foothills of the Sierra—don't forget the Sierra has foothills, too.

I did not make myself clear if I left you with the impression that they are going to be willing allies of our position. I ask you to ask yourself whether we should not be allies of their position, instead of they of ours. Because, I want to repeat, the big payoff in relating man to nature, as Dr. Condliffe suggested, is on economic grounds, and not in the realm of wildlife, weekends, and vacations.

There's plenty of need for maintaining wilderness, but if more men can live and work day-by-day closer to their natural environment, I think the values of wilderness will be immeasurably strengthened. What I am suggesting—without in any way endangering our own program of supporting wildlands and recreational facilities—is that we should think more sympathetically about the common man's interests regarding the same basic values of nature, but expressed in terms of these simpler ways of living and of making a living.

So, I really am asking us to do something re-constructive, re-creational, if you will, about our own thinking instead of going onto the hustings and urging the great mass of people merely to vote for our favorite legislation and ideas about wilderness.

MODERATOR SIRI: Here's an intriguing question: "Can the Government buy land on time, or do they always have to pay cash?"

MR. HARTZOG: We occasionally buy on time. Since Congress has not authorized contract authorization (which would commit future Congresses to the appropriation of money for obligations entered into), we occasionally enter into deferred purchase contracts.

As a matter of fact, such authority exists in connection with the Point Reyes legislation right here in California. We have one or two of these deferred purchase contracts in Point Reyes right now.

MR. CLIFF: I might say the Sierra Club and nature conservationists helped out the National Park Service and the U.S. Forest Service at times when the U.S. Government did not have the money or was not able to appropriate it.

MODERATOR SIRI: This one, I think, can be answered very briefly: "Will Land and Water Conservation Fund moneys be available to local jurisdictions and counties, or just to states?"

MR. CRAFTS: It can be available to local jurisdictions, both counties and municipalities, provided the "State Outdoor Recreation Plan" includes all the counties and municipalities that meet the state's needs. There is specific language in the statute on this point, and this has been made very clear to the states as well as the local governments. I think almost without exception the states are including as part of their plan a certain amount of local governmental action. I know for our part that we are strongly pushing the states in that direction. However, the moneys themselves cannot directly come from the Federal Government to the local government but must go through the states.

MODERATOR SIRI: Here's another one for Mr. Hartzog: "There has been criticism of recent tendencies to build roads in national parks to unnecessarily high standards. This seems to apply particularly at the moment to Mount McKinley National Park. Do you have any comment, Mr. Hartzog?"

MR. HARTZOG: This is probably one of the most commented on questions that I have had any experience with recently. I have not been to Mount McKinley, and I have not seen that road. But about this question of roads: we are faced with a great problem in serving the needs of all kinds of visitors to national parks. This is why I commented specifically in my remarks earlier that we are going to explore in a great deal more depth the concept of this wilderness threshold, because I think there is a great opportunity to disperse this automotive traffic which we have. It is accepted in our way of life that one-way roads do not have to be built to the normal high standards of two-way traffic. I think also that we are face to face with some other hard decisions on which we need to get together—decisions requiring careful thought. As you bring more and more people into the out-of-doors, we conservationists have a great challenge to move these people in such a way that we preserve the values that permitted the establishment of these areas in the first place and still give a satisfying experience to these people.

This brings us to the question of mass transportation. Aren't there places where mechanical means of transportation offer greater protection to the parks as set aside than do the construction of roads? While I am unable to comment in detail about the Mount McKinley road, the end of the road is being downgraded to a lower standard than the beginning of it, according to my understanding from my regional director and chief of design office, who have been there.

MODERATOR SIRI: One last question: "Who is examining possible wilderness areas outside of the national parks and the national forests?"

MR. STODDARD: For potential wilderness areas, there are authorities in the Wilderness Act which provide a procedure for identifying and setting up these areas. We are in the process of inventorying the public lands to know, in turn, where they are, how large they are, what impact their preservation would have. It will probably be some time yet before we do have full information.

MR. CRAFTS: I might say also in connection with both the Fund Act and the nation-wide plan, which first will go to Congress a couple of years from now, the question of additional wilderness areas will be considered.

VI

LUNCHEON
April 3, 1965

———————

Introduction

PEGGY WAYBURN

Address

JOHN A. CARVER, Jr.

PEGGY WAYBURN, *Master of Ceremonies*

INTRODUCTION

→ *Peggy Wayburn*

I have asked the heads of the Federal agencies charged with administering our wilderness lands, our parks, and our forests to sit at the head table. These men—George Hartzog, Edward Cliff, Edward Crafts, and Charles Stoddard—need no introduction; you have heard from them earlier. But I wanted them to sit here in a place of honor so that we might publicly recognize them as men who are dedicated public servants in the highest sense of the word. We would like to think that they find in the Wilderness Conference a forum where they may bring their ideas and their plans and talk them over with friends. For we think of them as our friends.

The fifth gentleman here from Washington is our luncheon speaker today. Ed and I first met John Carver at a rather interesting affair. It was at the dedication of a road, a road whose location we had fought bitterly, the Tioga Road. The dedication took place on a beautiful mountain day. Ed sat on the speaker's platform, and he was the only person there dressed in mountain clothes. I always remember this because there were ladies in high heels and hats and gentlemen with ties and shirts and suits on, but Ed Wayburn had on a Tirolean hat and checked shirt and jeans. After the ceremony was over, we met John Carver who had come out as the new Assistant Secretary of the Department of the Interior for this dedication, and he took his coat off and he said, "You know, you folks are the only people here properly dressed for this occasion." Well, we thought then that this was a man who understood us. Maybe it is because he is from Idaho, but nothing that he has said or done since has altered our impression.

He has worked with and for us for conservation ends with great zeal. He is no longer assistant; he is now Under Secretary of the Interior. We are proud and honored indeed that he is here with us. May I introduce to you, John Carver.

ADDRESS

➸➸➸ *John A. Carver, Jr.*

Park Service Director George Hartzog was asked earlier, I'm told, about the State of California's letter to the Secretary of the Interior about the Redwoods proposal. I had an opportunity last night to discuss this briefly with Mr. Fisher and Mr. Hartzog, and this morning we talked with Secretary Udall about Mr. Fisher's letter on behalf of the State of California. The Secretary asked me to bring to you an informal response to the letter which we have received from California. He wanted me to tell you that the Department of the Interior very much prizes and values the attitude expressed by the State of California in working on this common problem. We recognize the great interest California has in this, and we know that California alone among public agencies has experience in the management of the redwood resource.

We are glad—as Director Hartzog told you—to have these very constructive comments by the State of California. We are determined to proceed as promptly as possible to evaluate all of the suggestions which have come through on our original proposal, and that will include a review of the suggestions which have been made by California.

The Secretary asked me to say that the question of the location of the park may well be up for discussion; but he wanted me to remind you that the charter we have from the President of the United States is for a Redwoods National Park.

We are going to stay within that charter from the President.

Last September the President of the United States signed into law the Wilderness Act. This is your first Biennial Conference since that historic occasion.

Considering the single-mindedness with which the goal of legislation was pursued for so long, it might seem to some quite remarkable that there is very little of the atmosphere of the victory celebration here today.

Was the quest the thing? Or is there the feeling that enactment of the legislation was only the signal for the beginning of a new task, one to equal or exceed both the importance and the difficulty of the effort to get a bill?

Legislation is the glamorous center ring in the public affairs circus tent. Many of you acquired considerable virtuosity in this specialized field, as you fought the long battle to get a Wilderness Bill. You learned how important timing is in a legislative struggle. You learned that some of the opposition you experienced, far from being grounded in base motives, were in fact traceable to legitimate and praiseworthy concern about matters going to the heart of our governmental system. Some of your reputed opponents were responsible for getting, in the end, a better bill.

So it will not be surprising if all the attention of some of you shifts to new struggles in the legislative arena. The authorization of a Redwoods National Park is a prime candidate for your attention, a stone upon which your legislative skills can be further tested and whetted.

If the legislative arena is the center ring, administration is the kitchen tent. Who can get excited about the process of devising Wilderness System regulations—of conducting surveys and reviews? Interpretation of the congressional language about reviews of roadless areas is for the lawyers and the bureaucrats.

Perhaps in making this speech I have the choice I've consigned to some of you. Perhaps I should kick off a drive for Redwood National Park legislation.

I shan't do so, although I will be willing, later, to answer questions on the subject if you wish to ask some. I myself am a kitchen hand. Wilderness legislation is a new kind of legislation, and for the administrator there is plenty of excitement and plenty of challenge in considering the whats and hows and whys of getting an act translated into a program. That is why I shall talk today mainly about implementation of the Wilderness Act.

We all know that ethical considerations are at the root of wilderness legislation. This is not new, for ethical considerations support a good deal of our lawmaking activity, hopefully all of it. Even in the field of laws for the administration of our natural resources, ethical bases have always been present, but in the past they have been those designed to serve a frontier nation, an expanding and developing nation.

As we've opened up the western country, as we've brought water to the desert, we have fashioned as we went along rules and principles which were rooted in sound common sense, and thus calculated to maintain a semblance of order—the doctrine of prior appropriation in water law, the rules of discovery and *pedis possessio* in the mining claim country, the 160-acre limitation of the reclamation homestead, and even provisions in most of our western state constitutions for eminent domain powers to force joint or common use of wagon roads, canals, and railroads.

It is not that our forefathers were unaware of natural beauty. The wonders of nature did have meaning to them. But in their scheme of things, the government got into such matters seldom, if at all. The flashes of vision shown by a Yellowstone Park Act in 1872 were special and isolated exceptions to the rule. Even in the private affairs of the time, concern for natural beauty was seldom accorded a very high priority.

To suggest that natural resources should be managed by government to satisfy the needs of the mind and spirit, as well as to meet physical and economic needs would once have been regarded as absurd. Thoreau enjoined no such duty upon government. Jefferson accepted the responsibility of civilized society to provide an environment wherein man might function to his best capacity, but he, too, saw it as a moral structure, not a governmental program object.

We've come a long way. It is a measure of the vitality of our system that as our population has grown, and as we've become crowded more and more upon each other, we have found that the ethical standards for management of land and resources have been heightened.

The process has been revolutionary, and not one, but two revolutions are involved.

The two separate revolutionary ideas which have converged upon the Federal Government in point of time in this decade are: (1) a governmental concern for outdoor recreation in its broadest aspects, and (2) a governmental concern for the quality of man's total environment. The convergence has caused confusion, for many people think of the two as the same.

Even my admired friend, Luna Leopold, seems to fall momentarily into this confusion in his fine paper already read to this Conference.

In that paper he groups together the maintaining and enhancing of landscape quality and the moral concern for our ecological environment, as part and parcel with outdoor recreation. He puts both under the same heading of social objectives which may not be amenable to "multiple-use" handling.

But he does point out that for "wilderness recreation" any regular utilization is detrimental, and thus he zeroes in on the dilemma.

I don't care to try to justify wilderness legislation as recreation legislation, or to make "wilderness" a specialized kind of recreation. Rather, I see wilderness as a new and heightened ethical concept governing the management of natural resources. The Wilderness Act is concerned with the management of natural resources committed to the stewardship of the Federal Government.

In this age of maturity of our society, we have come to the realization that the land itself, which is the base not only of habitation and of food, fuel, fiber, and minerals, contains also certain soul-satisfying elements. We have come to see that these may be both vital and exhaustible.

The steward's task is to manage the resource base according to the policies set forth by the Congress. The Congress has added a new objective for this management and has called it "wilderness."

The addition, however satisfying intellectually or emotionally, complicates the management task. For the manager must now accommodate conflicting contentions as to what standard for wilderness really was intended by the Congress. The procedure for that accommodation is the rule making and the administrative process. For me this is the primary unfinished wilderness agenda.

Fortunately, the Congress took direct responsibility for a major segment of the task when it placed 9.1 million acres of national forest wilderness into the Wilderness System. And it specified that additions had to have legislative approval. But it also provided that the Department of the Interior should remain responsible for administering the mining laws and mineral leasing laws under special provisions of the Act. In this connection, the House and Senate conferees, in reporting and recommending a compromise Wilderness Bill to the Congress made the following statement:

"The conference committee expects that the mining industry and the agencies of the Department of the Interior will explore existing Primitive Areas so that when legislation pertaining to such Primitive Areas is considered at a later date, Congress will have the benefit of professional technical advice as to the presence or absence of minerals in each area."

Regulations implementing these special provisions are reaching final draft form. When ready, they will be exposed to public scrutiny and public discussion. You have a stake, a major stake, in these discussions.

We already know the general shape of a major problem facing the Interior Department with respect to the national forest Primitive Areas—5.5 million acres not yet within the System.

What are these "mineral surveys" supposed to do?

The Act directs the U.S. Geological Survey and the U.S. Bureau of Mines to undertake planned, recurring surveys in national forest wilderness to determine mineral values, and to report the results to the Congress and the public.

The same requirement may extend to other Federal lands being reviewed for possible inclusion, where such lands are at present open to mineral prospecting, leasing, location, or entry.

If the process of administration in this difficult area is, as I think, the process of presenting identified choices to the public, then one philosophy to support the making of the mineral surveys is evident. An intelligent choice between the program ascendancy of esthetic values and of material values can be made only as reliable knowledge is available as to the nature and extent of both of these values. Where mineral or material potential is absent or slight, the wilderness values have little or no competition.

Admittedly, this doesn't help in making a choice where the mineral or material potential is substantial; but here two subordinate choices or alternatives are open. One is the choice to defer the ultimate decision. We can consciously choose to leave the ultimate choice to the next generation.

But this kind of choice is unsatisfactory on several counts, without at least some general knowledge of the mineral values. For example, one mineral may be much more vital than another, or the trend of demand may be up or down.

The other choice requires even more specialized knowledge. We have the choice of consciously paying a higher price for available substitutes or modifications for the material values whose use is to be denied.

In some areas of decision making, this is comparatively routine—

routing a highway around a site of historical value, or around a wild-life refuge, for example.

But reliable knowledge is essential.

I bring these matters up because I have the impression that there were, in fact, two schools of thought in the Congress when the mineral survey provisions were agreed to.

Whether there was or was not a congressional intent for a *special* effort by the Government to survey above and beyond normal Geological Survey activities is not an easy question to answer.

The interpretation of the congressional mandate will involve further legislative consideration in the appropriation process, for it is before this forum that the conflicting views will be presented.

For some, the course to be taken is best stated in terms of ordinary program objectives. The Geological Survey assures that its surveys, although held to a level of reconnaissance for the most part, will be comprehensive, objective, and responsible, and that they will provide the penetrating analysis of mineral potential that the nation needs for intelligent planning for resource utilization and preservation.

A determination about whether there is *any* mineral in an area is a geologist's job. Depending on the intensity of his survey, he may be able to qualify his findings with tolerable precision.

But the decision about whether *any* volume is economically significant is a decision for economists and business managers. And the recent history of mining law, both in executive department administration and before the courts, demonstrates that judgments about the economic significance of mineral deposits are very complex and highly controversial.

Then even after some measures can be worked out on mineral values, there still remains the decision relating its significance to the philosophy and intent of the Wilderness Act. *That* decision is fundamentally a *political* one.

It is fortunate that the hard choices probably will be few in number. Reporting of areas as containing *no* valuable or potentially valuable minerals, doubtful though some of the miners may remain, eliminates a large part of the argument.

So, also, we are assured that even large ore bodies are relatively small in terms of acreages involved, by definition, in wilderness situations. And, fortunately, sophisticated means of removal and access involving least detriment are feasible if material values are high.

The typical wilderness situation is not notable for the occurrence of valuable minerals, and we do not expect that large areas will prove to be mineral bearing.

Still, when the chips are all down, choices have to be made, including the immediate choice of how to plan for mineral surveys in the Primitive Areas. As to this, I must hope that we will be guided by intelligence and knowledge. The Department has always had the duty to identify potential mineral-bearing areas and to furnish the information to the public and the Congress.

The Wilderness Act did more than establish a legislative policy and standard for wilderness preservation. It put into action a standard of governmental survey and review of resource values conducted in the daylight of public scrutiny.

The procedure seems complex, but it contains important guarantees. The ten-year review schedule assures against undue delays.

No one can say exactly what the future holds, but the net outcome can't help being a growing National Wilderness Preservation System under the firm protection of statutory law.

President Johnson has said: "Only in this country have such positive measures been taken to preserve the wilderness adequately for its scenic and spiritual wealth . . . The Congress can justly be proud of the contribution of foresight and prudent planning expressed by this measure to perpetuate our rare and rich natural heritage."

His message of February 8, 1965, to the Congress on the National Wilderness Preservation System stated:

> The wonder of Nature is the treasure of America.
> What we have in woods and forest, valley and stream, in the gorges and the mountains and the hills, we must not destroy. The precious legacy of preservation of beauty will be our gift to posterity.

The President also has expressed in his Natural Beauty Message a desire to "proceed on schedule with studies required to define and enlarge the Wilderness System as established by the 88th Congress."

With your cooperation and the cooperation of others—and under close and constant public scrutiny—we intend to do our part in this noble effort to preserve the wonder of nature as the treasure of America.

louds over Grand Canyon National Park   *Ansel Adams*

"From this green earth . . ."

> For I have learned
> To look on nature, not as in the hour
> Of thoughtless youth, but hearing oftentimes
> The still sad music of humanity,
> Nor harsh nor grating, though of ample power
> To chasten and subdue. And I have felt
> A presence that disturbs me with the joy
> Of elevated thoughts; a sense sublime
> Of something far more deeply interfused,
> Whose dwelling is the light of setting suns,
> And the round ocean, and the living air,
> And the blue sky, and in the mind of man,
> A motion and a spirit, that impels
> All thinking things, all objects of all thought,
> And rolls through all things. Therefore am I still
> A lover of the meadows and the woods,
> And mountains; and of all that we behold
> From this green earth; of all the mighty world
> Of eye and ear, both what they half create,
> And what perceive; well pleased to recognize
> In nature and the language of the sense,
> The anchor of my purest thoughts, the nurse,
> The guide, the guardian of my heart, and soul
> Of all my moral being.—WILLIAM WORDSWORTH

Sierra shoreline
by Cedric Wright

Leaping water
by Cedric Wright

Spring Pool Canyon Bar,
Glen Canyon
by Philip Hyde

*Junipers
at timberline
by Cedric Wright*

Pasture, Sonoma County, California

Ansel Adams (courtesy American Trust Company)

Forest floor   *Steve Crouch*

Wordsworth poem, "Lines Composed a Few Miles Above Tintern Abbey
on Revisiting the Banks of the Wye During a Tour, July 13, 1798,"
as quoted by Ashley Montagu

VII

WHAT WILDERNESS MEANS TO MAN

_____

Introduction

EDGAR WAYBURN

The Spiritual Need

SIGURD F. OLSON

Wilderness and Humanity

ASHLEY MONTAGU

Wilderness—A Psychiatric Necessity

WILLIAM C. GIBSON

Facets of Wilderness

MARGARET W. OWINGS

Summary of the Conference

HAROLD GILLIAM

EDGAR WAYBURN: *Chairman*

INTRODUCTION

➤ Edgar Wayburn

To reach a solution on anything one needs to have the "what, how, when, where, and why." During the earlier part of the conference, we have heard extremely knowledgeable and able speakers discuss most aspects of the problem of wilderness. But all have simply set the stage for this session on "why wilderness?"

We are part of a great crusade, which may perhaps be described as a counter-current against the tide of a technological and urbanizing civilization. At the same time we are a positive force for the retention of our natural environment and the spiritual and healthful sustenance it can give us. Deep in man's nature is the need for spiritual and cultural identification. Each of us may express it differently. William Herbert Carruth, in his poem "Each in His Own Tongue," wrote:

> *A haze on the far horizon,*
> *The infinite, tender sky,*
> *The ripe, rich tint of the cornfields,*
> *And the wild geese sailing high;*
> *And all over a plain and lowland,*
> *The charm of the goldenrod—*
> *Some of us call it Autumn,*
> *And others call it God.*
> *Like tides on a crescent sea beach,*
> *When the moon is new and thin,*
> *Into our hearts high yearnings*
> *Come welling and surging in—*
> *Come from the mystic ocean*
> *Whose rim no foot has trod—*
> *Some of us call it longing,*
> *And others call it God.*

Our discussants this afternoon will explore the "why" in depth.

THE SPIRITUAL NEED

→≫ *Sigurd F. Olson*

I am happy to talk about the spiritual values of wilderness because I feel they are all important—the real reason for all the practical things we must do to save wilderness. In the last analysis it is the spiritual values we are really fighting to preserve.

Not all look to the wilderness for spiritual sustenance. Some seem to get along very well without it, finding their values in different ways. Others must know wilderness at first hand, must experience it physically, as well as spiritually. There is a great diversity in wilderness appreciation and wilderness need; but I have discovered in a lifetime of traveling in primitive regions, a lifetime of seeing people living in the wilderness and using it, that there is a hard core of wilderness need in everyone, a core that makes its spiritual values a basic human necessity. There is no hiding it. The core is there, no matter how sophisticated, blasé, and urban one might be. Deep down inside of us all is a need of wilderness.

I shall not attempt to enter the vast realm of religious belief or the concept of a Diety, though there is close correlation between them and the spiritual values of wilderness which in themselves are only one facet of the entire complex, a facet which cannot be disregarded in probing the problem of man's relationship to God and the universe.

In order to speak intelligently about such intangibles as the spiritual, we must attempt to define them, for they are often misunderstood and impossible to measure by ordinary standards. We are accustomed to associate the spiritual with such immortal lines as, "He leadeth me beside still waters; He annointeth my soul"; or "I lift up mine eyes to the hills from whence cometh my help." No one needs to explain or define the meaning of such expressions, for we sense intuitively and from long association and personal experience the joy and lift of spirit they epitomize. Even those who think wilderness means nothing share in this reaction to visions that actually had their origin in the ancient concept of far horizons, beauty, and silence.

There is far more, however, to the spiritual values of wilderness than the beautiful music of the Psalms and the emotional release they bring. Webster, in defining the spiritual, speaks of the soul, the essence, eternal values as opposed to the worldly or carnal—the imponderables as against the tangibles. A philosophy is involved, a way of looking at life, and a perspective that goes deeply into value judgments that affect our happiness.

We might argue any of these points and try to explain or analyze, as many have done before us. Volumes have been written by theologians and philosophers on their meaning, but the more exhaustively we delve into the discussions, the more we are convinced that argument is futile in view of the differences in individual understanding and belief stemming from reactions that range from the faintest glimmerings in comprehension to the ultimate beatific vision of the saints and prophets.

On one point all agree: that spiritual values contribute to joy and richness of living; that without them existence lacks color and warmth, and the soul itself is drab and impoverished. We accept the broad premise that such values, inspired by the contemplation of wilderness beauty and mystery, were the well springs of our dawning culture and the first significant expressions of the human mind. True in the nebulous past, it is as true today no matter how life has changed or what has happened to our environment.

I am confident that Stone Age man who some forty thousand years ago painted his symbols on the caves of France and Spain was powerfully stirred by the mystery of the unknown and the spirit world that dwelt there. Such surviving examples of prehistoric art tell of the millenia when man pondered his environment as an awareness finally dawned that the dreams, longings, fears, and hopes that haunted him could be translated into forms of meaning and permanence. Symbols from which spells and magic went forth to influence hunting, fertility, and success in his various ventures—they represented the growing world of the spirit, the first indications of the mighty concept of immortality, and the realization that after death men would dwell forever in the vast vault of the heavens. It was then he emerged from the dark abyss of his past into a world of mind and soul and began to give form to his deepest and most profound emotions.

But why, we ask, does modern man, now almost completely removed from his wilderness background, still look to the hills for his spiritual help in meeting the tensions and pressures of this age? Why does he yearn for open space and naturalness, for the sea with its immensities, for vistas across valleys and mountain ranges? Why on weekends and holidays does he stream from his crowded and clamorous cities into the open countryside?

Anthropologically, the answer is simple. A hundred thousand years have elapsed since man's emergence from the primitive, perhaps a million or more if we go back to the very beginnings of the race to which he belongs. During all this time he lived close to the earth, regulating his life by the seasons, hunting his food, knowing the fears, challenges, and satisfactions of a life entirely dependent upon nature. Only during the last forty thousand years did he develop any sort of culture and not until ten thousand years ago leave any evidence of historical record. Until the last century the broad pattern of his life had actually varied little. To be sure, there were cities long before that, but the vast majority of people lived on the land or in small rural communities still close to the influences of the past. Then in the space of a few decades, he was literally hurled into a machine age of whirring speed and complexity where the ancient ecological and emotional balances were upset and his way of life utterly changed.

In the light of his primitive conditioning, man is still part of the past, responsive to and dependent upon the type of environment from which he came. Adaptations come slowly in all creatures and man is no exception. When weary and confused by the life he is now leading, it is no wonder he longs to escape from the barriers he has built around himself. It is natural for him to dream of freedom and to look backward to a time when life was simpler, to old familiar trails where the terrain is known. There seems to be an almost universal urge, no matter what the stage of man's sophistication or removal from the natural, to align himself somehow with those forces and influences that were dominant for ages.

Stanley Diamond said: "The longing for a primitive mode of existence is no mere fantasy or sentimental whim; it is consonant with fundamental human needs. . . . The search for the primitive is as old as civilization. It is the search for the utopia of the past projected into the future; it is paradise lost and paradise regained . . . inseparable from the vision of civilization."

A man may not really know why he climbs a mountain, crosses a desert, travels by canoe down some strange waterway, or sees the national parks or the wilderness areas of the national forests from the comfort of an automobile. Somehow in spite of himself, the spiritual penetrates his consciousness, and he absorbs a sense of vastness, far horizons, and silence plus other intangibles always found away from cities and towns. It may not be realized until afterward, but in some moment of quiet remembering, the essence of wildness comes to him like an almost forgotten dream—the inevitable aftermath, the spiritual values responsible for the glow and the inner satisfactions such experiences leave.

Man's great problem today is to make the transition, to bridge the gap between the old world and the new, to understand the reason for his discontent with things as they are, and to recognize the solution. His old world of superstition, evil spirits, and fear is gone. Gone too his dependence on the wilderness and his sense of close relationship, belonging, and animal oneness with the earth and the life around him. He must recognize now that while some of his spiritual roots have been severed, he still has his gods, and that his attitude toward wilderness has entered a new phase in which for the first time in his evolution as a thinking, perceptive creature, he can look at it with understanding and appreciation of its deeper meanings, knowing that within its borders may be the answer to his longing for naturalness. He needs to know that the spiritual values that once sustained him are still there in the timelessness and majestic rhythms of those parts of the world he has not ravished.

With this realization, wilderness assumes new and great significance. It concerns all of humanity and has philosophical implications that give breadth to the mind and nourish the spirit. Because man's subconscious is steeped in the primitive, looking to the wilderness actually means a coming home to him, a moving into ancient grooves of human and prehuman experience. So powerful is the impact of returning that whether a man realizes it or not, reactions are automatically set in motion that bring in their train an uplift of the spirit. It is as though, tormented by some inner and seemingly unsolvable problem, he is suddenly released from frustration and perplexity and sees his way.

One of the great challenges confronting those who believe in the preservation of wilderness is to build a broader base of values than physical recreation, a base of sufficient depth and solidity to counter the charge that it exists for only a privileged and hardy few. Should this be possible, and I believe it is through stressing its all encompassing humanitarian values, then there will no longer be any question of its importance to mankind. Only when the true significance of wilderness is fully understood will it be safe from those who would despoil it.

Josef Pieper, a German philosopher, in speaking of the meaning of leisure, said it is a form of silence, a receptive and contemplative attitude of mind and soul, and a capacity for steeping oneself in the whole of creation. He might just as well have been explaining man's attitude in approaching the wilderness.

He quotes Plato who said: "But the gods, taking pity on mankind born to work, laid down a succession of recurring feasts to restore them from their fatigue so that nourishing themselves in festive companionship with the gods, they should again stand upright and erect."

Companionship with the gods and true leisure—this is perhaps what modern man seeks when he goes to the wilderness. This much we know is true: that while a man is with his gods, no matter who they may be, he can forget the problems and petty distractions of the workaday world and reach out to spiritual realizations that renew him. Only through receptiveness, contemplation, and awareness does anyone open himself to the great intuitions and consciousness of what life and the universe really mean.

Thomas Aquinas once said: "To know the universal essence of things is to reach a point of view from which the whole of being and all existing things become visible; and at the same time the spiritual outpost so reached enables man to look at the landscape of the universe."

I like the idea of looking at the landscape of the universe, for it condenses into one shining vision the whole concept of spiritual experience. By "essence" Aquinas means the reality of man's relationship to the universe of which he is a part. If a man can sense this, if he can even glimpse the infinity Aquinas talks about, he might see the landscape of the universe.

Some years ago, I accompanied the famous geologist and geographer Wallace Atwood on a glacialogical survey of the Quetico-Superior country. We wanted to see what had happened to the old pre-glacial stream patterns of the rivers which ages ago carried the wreckage of the awesome Laurentian Mountains toward the seas of the south.

We sat before our fire one night and talked about what we had seen, but mostly we admired the beautiful specimens of porphyry we had found on Lake Saganaga. Dr. Atwood had a prize specimen in his hand, and as he turned it over and over allowing the firelight to strike its crystals, his eyes shone.

"Tell me," I said finally, "how is it that near the age of eighty you still get as much pleasure and excitement out of finding a new specimen as though you were a geology student on his first field trip?"

He gazed into the fire awhile before answering. "The secret," he said, "is never to lose the power of wonder. If you keep that alive, you stay young forever. If you lose it, you die."

I have never forgotten what he said, and I know now that the power of wonder is back of all creative thought and effort, and without it scientists, artists, and thinkers in all disciplines would lose the spur and challenge to learn and explore the mysteries about them. Wonder becomes then a spiritual value, the basic source of energy and inspiration in the evolution of the mind of man. Though we may produce life and eventually know the answers to all the secrets, we must never forget that wonder was responsible.

Albert Einstein reaffirmed this truth when he said: "The most beautiful experience we can have is the mysterious. It is the fundamental emotion which stands at the cradle of true art and true science. I am satisfied with the mystery of the eternity of life and of being able, through awareness of glimpsing the marvelous structure of the existing world together with the devoted striving, to comprehend a portion of it, be it ever so tiny, of the Reason that manifests itself in nature."

Over the centuries a host of other great minds have also believed that if through awareness and wonder man might recognize even faintly his personal relationship to the universe, he would then partake and become part of the order and reason that governs his existence, the movement of galaxies, as well as the minutest divisions of matter. From the early scriptures and through all cultures, this profound concept has echoed and re-echoed as man realized its immensity and spiritual connotations. A grand concept, it has increased the stature of man and stood the test of time.

Prerequisite to understanding the lofty ideas of Plato and Aquinas is developing the capacity of awareness and wonder. If this ability is one of the important potentials of man, and the quality of inciting it one of the spiritual values of wilderness, here is an opportunity; for only by encouraging wonder in others and explaining to millions of people its true meaning, can we ever be sure of preserving any wilderness on our planet.

When Aquinas, in speaking of wonder, said: "Man's first experience with it sets his feet on the ladder that may lead to beatific vision," he meant what to him and other seers was the supreme climax of spiritual revelation.

The late Pierre Teilhard de Chardin, one of the loftiest minds of this age, in speaking of such moments said: "But now the atmosphere around him becomes sustaining, consistent and warm. As he awakens to a sense of universal unification, a wave of new life penetrates to the fiber and marrow of the least of his undertakings and the least of his desires. Everything glows as if impregnated with the essential flavor of the absolute, showing our accession beyond all ideologies and systems to a different and higher sphere, a new spiritual dimension."

While it is good to know how great minds feel and to bask in the aura of their perception, we realize we are ordinary men who must, in order to understand, translate such experiences into concepts that can be applied to the problems of living in an age seemingly dedicated to the destruction of ancient values and our environment. What can we deduce from their expressions that bear on the kind of wilderness experience we are concerned with? Is there anything tangible we can apply to life as we know it? What broad conclusions from their flights into mystery and revelation can we use? They speak of oneness and unity with life and the universe, of the eternal essence, and the perception of reality. What exactly does this mean to us?

Lewis Mumford gave us a clue when he said, "Man's biological survival is actually involved in cosmic processes, and he prospers best when some sense of cosmic purpose attends his daily activities."

Wilderness offers this sense of cosmic purpose if we open our hearts and minds to its possibilities. It may come in such moments of revelation as Aquinas, Chardin, and others speak about, burning instants of truth when everything stands clear. It may come as a slow realization after long periods of waiting. Whenever it comes, life is suddenly illumined, beautiful, and transcendent, and we are filled with awe and deep happiness. All of us have known such moments but seldom recognized them at the time or comprehended their meaning. At least so it is with me and possibly with most of us whose experiences have come to us in the wilds.

I remember several such moments—an evening when I had climbed to the summit of Robinson Peak in the Quetico to watch the sunset: the flaming ball trembling on the very edge of a far ridge—fluid, alive, pulsating. As I watched it sink slowly into the dusk, it seemed to me I could actually feel the earth turning away from it, and sense its rotation.

Once many years ago, I stood gazing down a wilderness waterway with a fleet of rocky islands floating in the distance. The loons were calling, echoes rolling back from the shores and from unknown lakes across the ridges until the dusk seemed alive with their music. I was aware then of a fusion with the country, an overwhelming sense of completion in which all my hopes and experiences seemed concentrated in the moment before me.

I shall not attempt to analyze my reactions nor correlate them with order or reason, and I believe to try would be a mistake. I was not particularly aware of destiny or my role in the great plan. What I did carry away with me was a sense of wonder and deep contentment, a certain feeling of wholeness and fulfillment as though I needed nothing more. It would take a greater and more perceptive mind than mine to explain their full significance, and were they to do so, they might discover our moments of revelation were the same.

Life as it is lived for most people today is a fragmentary sort of thing, and man often feels as impermanent and transitory as the things he has built. If through such experiences as these he can somehow catch a feeling of wholeness or a hint of cosmic consciousness, he will know what the sages have been trying to tell us. No two people have the same type of experience, nor do they ever come in identical ways or similar situations. When I think of man's spiritual need of wilderness, I believe that the opportunity of being aware of and knowing such moments is an important part of it.

If as Harrison Brown said, "The spiritual resources of man are the critical resources," then wilderness which fosters such values must be preserved. If we can believe what the wise have said for thousands of years, then there is hope for wildness and beauty in our environment. If spirit is a power and a force that spells the difference between richness of living and sterility, then we know what we must do. It may well be that with our swiftly expanding population, the movement away from nature into vast city complexes and the decimation facing much of the land, that the wilderness we can hold now will become the final bastions of the spirit of man. Unless we can preserve places where the endless spiritual needs of man can be fulfilled and nourished, we will destroy our culture and ourselves.

WILDERNESS AND HUMANITY

⇛ Ashley Montagu

Some weeks ago a cartoonist, clearly painfully aware of what has been going on around him, produced a cartoon showing two obviously opulent men standing amidst a host of oil derricks and the splintered remnants of trees by a pool filled with oil slick and debris. With evident pride one of these instruments of destruction, surveying the devastation they had jointly wrought, remarks to the other, "And to think that only a few weeks ago all this was wilderness."

That cartoon faithfully recorded an incident which must have been repeated scores of thousands of times in the United States alone, not to mention other lands. A short time ago I read in the *New York Times* an account of a developer who had announced his intention of erecting a housing project on one of the last remaining woods in Long Island. The residents, revolted by the threatened destruction, called a meeting of protest at which the developer presented his case. He failed to understand, he said, how there could possibly be the least objection to his proposed leveling of the woodland, and with a sincerity that could only have sprung from the deepest conviction, he pleadingly said, "But, look what beautiful houses, streets, roadways and gas stations there would be where now there is only wilderness." It was, in its way, really quite touching, for I am informed that he had a catch in his voice. He doubtless felt as Milton might have done had his *Paradise Lost* been rejected by an uncomprehending editor. What the outcome of the meeting was I do not know, but I suspect that the developer won out, and that for him the destruction of the woodland and its replacement by a development assumed the form of *Paradise Regained*. Like Peter Bell:

> *A primrose by a river's brim*
> *A yellow primrose was to him,*
> *And it was nothing more.*

There can be little doubt that there are among us, in numbers saddening to reflect upon, many who when they see a blade of grass or a tree immediately feel how nice it would be if it could be bulldozed out of existence and a surface of asphalt put in its place. Wilderness is equated to wasteland, and with the pressures of population being what they are, there remain few among us who seem able to contemplate with equanimity good land going to what they consider waste.

Wherever one may live, it is not necessary to travel far to observe the human and natural devastation that is everywhere about us, the debasement of the human spirit, the disinheritance of the birthright of millions of human beings, the disengagement from humanity, the progression from cruelty to callousness to indifference to unawareness. This is the condition of millions of human beings, the product of over-population, of what inevitably occurs when human beings uncontrolledly, thoughtlessly, unfeelingly, and irresponsibly do as they please.

If the human landscape has been devastated, what shall one say of the rapine and spoilation of the natural landscape, of the wilderness, the congenial environment in which man once lived? Here there has been not only destruction of the natural beauties of the land but also an unspeakable transmogrification and uglification of it. The living creatures that once inhabited the land are everywhere threatened with extinction. Numberless animals, every day, birds and butterflies, beautiful and enhancing, cease to be before the onrushing masses of reduplicating human beings and the poisons they produce. The air, the land, rivers, lakes, and streams are unconscionably polluted, while the silent spring bears poignant testimony to the degradation of the human spirit. As Aldous Huxley remarked after reading Rachel Carson's book, we are exterminating half the basis of English poetry. And as the editor of the *Architectural Forum* put it in the title of a significant book, we are turning God's Own Country into *God's Own Junkyard,* as anyone who travels along our highways may see for himself.

Perhaps the greatest havoc wrought by the pressures of population has been the damage to the human spirit, disabling millions of human beings from the ability to perceive and to feel as human beings. Conditioned in a world which places an exaggerated value upon things, these persons take such things for granted, perceiving what they see only as things, not in the least in the context of the human situation, in the context of the necessity of beauty, and scarcely ever being humanly affronted by them. On the other hand, they rejoice in the great highways and freeways that have brought about the destruction of millions of trees, the annihilation of parklands, farmlands, meadows, orchards, and the wilderness. And to what end? So that the slums of the immediate future may replace them in order to house the millions who will require the sewers, the gasoline stations, shopping centers, hot dog stands, drive-ins, and other desecrations of the landscape which, like a cancerous growth, spread over the length and breadth of the land destroying everything beautiful or potentially beautiful in their path.

These desecrations are a cancer from which a great part of the inhabited world is increasingly suffering. Unless we quickly learn to understand the causes of this disorder, we shall be overcome by our own misguided thrust toward survival. This is no empty Jeremiad, for man's survival depends on his ability to care for and use his natural resources.

Contemporary man in relation to the wilderness is well described in A. E. Housman's "improvement" on Frances Cornford's poem "To a Fat Lady Seen from the Train."

> *O why do you walk through the fields in boots,*
> *Missing so much and so much?*
> *O fat white person whom nobody shoots,*
> *Why do you walk through the fields in boots,*
> *When the grass is soft as the breast of coots*
> *And shivering-sweet to the touch?*
> *O why do you walk through the fields in boots,*
> *Missing so much and so much?*

It was not always so. Man has been on this earth for about two million years, and for almost the whole of that time he lived in the wilderness; it was his home and his world. And of that world he considered himself a natural part. He was a food gatherer and hunter, and he saw and experienced the world as a web of intricate interrelationships of which he, in common with every other living thing—everything indeed, in nature—was an inseparable and connected part.

Such peoples, living as close to nature as they do, entertain a wholly different conception of their relation to the world in which they live from that of the town dweller of civilized societies. Indeed, the modern urbanite is so far removed from the world of nature, while his views of his own relation to the world in which he finds himself differ so profoundly from those of peoples living closer to nature that he usually finds it difficult, if not impossible, to understand the meaning of such peoples' beliefs. He, therefore, tends to treat them as odd, curious, esoteric, primitive, savage, wild, and strange. So far has urban man departed from life in the wilderness that he comes to regard it as something crude and rude, "wild" in the worser meaning of that word. Like his conception of "wild" animals, his view of the wilderness is as far removed from the realities as it could possibly be. A strong case might, in fact, be made for civilized man being the only "wild" animal in existence. Animals in the state of nature do not make war upon their own kind; they have no Attilas or Hitlers. They seldom exhibit the kind of savagery that civilized men exhibit toward one another. Civilized man, especially in the western world, has projected an image of his own violent self upon the screen of nature. Without in any way wishing to diminish the great contribution of Darwin toward our understanding of nature, his view of nature, as Patrick Geddes was the first to point out, was substantially a projection of conditions prevailing in 19th Century industrial Europe upon the backdrop of nature. One of Darwin's favorite phrases in *The Origin of Species* was "the warfare of Nature." It was an idea that Darwin inherited from earlier thinkers and from his environment. The conception of nature as a gladiatorial show is one which the followers of Darwin even more than Darwin himself helped to perpetuate. For most people today the idea of nature as the "wild," the "jungle," in the Darwinian sense, is the only idea of nature they know.

The myth of the beast and the myth of the jungle (as the mythological beliefs relating to wild animals and nature may be called) profoundly affect the attitudes and conduct of those who adhere to such myths toward the "wilderness." Seen through the distorting glass of their prejudices, the wilderness is something to be civilized, brought under control. The best way to do that is, of course, to get rid of it and to turn its "useless" acres to profitable use. Under the pressures of expanding populations, this has everywhere been the history of the destruction of the wilderness. Under the increasingly accelerating pressures of population everywhere in the inhabited world, millions of acres of wilderness are destined to be destroyed. It is, therefore, all the more necessary to do what we can now to make clear to everyone what such devastation is likely to do to humanity. In this way, perhaps, we may yet be able to save some remnants of the wilderness and also help to revitalize and renew man's necessary relationship to it.

Man, it cannot too often be pointed out, is a wild animal who has, in civilized societies, domesticated himself. Urban man especially lives under highly artificial conditions, in most cases far removed from the wilderness. Millions of such dwellers have never seen an apple on a tree, and the only animals they know are domestic ones and those they may have seen in zoos. This virtual complete separation from nature leads to a view of it which is wholly disengaged, even alienated, and frequently hostile. This is a pathological state, a morbid dissociation from what should have been a vital involvement in relation to the whole of nature. Man's two million or so years spent in close interrelationship with the wilderness helped to form him and make possible everything he has since done, and yet I believe with Benjamin Rush, that, "Man is naturally a wild animal . . . taken from the woods, he is never happy . . . till he returns to them again." This should not be taken to mean that there exists anything like an archetypal species memory, but what I think it should be taken to mean is that man is a part of the wilderness, a part of nature, and that his relation to it is not merely one of natural harmony and ecologic necessity, but also of civilized health. A healthy relationship to the wilderness is not in the least incompatible with civilized living. Indeed, I believe it to be an indispensable condition thereof; that no man is truly civilized unless he is involved in and cares for the wilderness. To live in the city can be quite wonderful and enlarging, but not if it renders one insensitive to the meaning of the wilderness. Detachment from the wilderness means detachment from the world of nature, an exchange of the one for attachment to the world of things. Most people feel this and hence the strong urge that so often comes upon them to return to the wilderness. The enormous number of people who enjoy camping with their families in the wilderness, and even those who prefer more sophisticated reversions to the wilderness such as a country or seashore hotel, or those Isles of Illusion, Palm Springs and Las Vegas, constitute a significant testimony not merely to the desire for a change of scene, but to the deep-seated need to get out into the open. It is a feeling beautifully expressed in Keats' sonnet,

> To one who has been long in city pent,
>   'Tis very sweet to look into the fair
>   And open face of heaven—to breathe a prayer
> Full in the smile of the blue firmament.
> Who is more happy, when, with heart's content,
>   Fatigued he sinks into some pleasant lair
>   Of wavy grass, and reads a debonair
> And gentle tale of love and languishment?

Returning home at evening, with an ear
  Catching the notes of Philomel—an eye
Watching the sailing cloudlet's bright career,
  He mourns that day so soon has glided by:
E'en like the passage of an angel's tear
  That falls through the clear ether silently.

Perhaps no other poet has put it better than Wordsworth in his "Lines Composed a Few Miles Above Tintern Abbey, on Revisiting the Banks of the Wye During a Tour, July 13, 1798."

                    For I have learned
To look on nature, not as in the hour
Of thoughtless youth, but hearing oftentimes
The still sad music of humanity,
Nor harsh nor grating, though of ample power
To chasten and subdue. And I have felt
A presence that disturbs me with the joy
Of elevated thoughts; a sense sublime
Of something far more deeply interfused,
Whose dwelling is the light of setting suns,
And the round ocean, and the living air,
And the blue sky, and in the mind of man,
A motion and a spirit, that impels
All thinking things, all objects of all thought,
And rolls through all things. Therefore am I still
A lover of the meadows and the woods,
And mountains; and of all that we behold
From this green earth; of all the mighty world
Of eye and ear, both what they half create,
And what perceive; well pleased to recognize
In nature and the language of the sense,
The anchor of my purest thoughts, the nurse,
The guide, the guardian of my heart, and soul
Of all my moral being.

To be cut off from the wilderness is to suffer a spiritual impoverishment and curtailment of life which the understanding and appreciation of the wilderness and the kinship with nature and everything in it, brings. It is not the notion of the wilderness for its own sake that is of value, but the awareness of one's relatedness to it, one's unity with it, that deepens and extends the scope of human life. The esthetic life and the enjoyment of the merely picturesque often lead to a sybaritic self-indulgence rather than to spiritual exaltation. And neither the one nor the other are enough, for what is necessary is the recognition of the simple fact that our wholeness as human beings depends upon the depth of our awareness of the fact that we are a part of the wholeness of nature, and that the standards of dominance we have erected for ourselves in relation to nature are artificial and destructive. As Immanuel Kant remarked, evolution has been anthropocentrically envisaged as "a very long ladder, created by man to place himself on the highest rung." And so we have created categories of "higher" and "lower" animals, a kind of race prejudice from the folly of which the "highest" so-called may justifiably do with the "lowest" so-called whatever they opportunistically desire. It is alleged that man is made in God's image, but that the beast is made in the image of the brute. Man, it is alleged, is loving and intelligent, the most successful of all creatures, and therefore superior to all other creatures, who act from instinct and not from intelligence, from selfish appetite and not from love. These are among the most entrenched beliefs of the learned as well as of the ignorant.

It is all very well awarding ourselves prizes for extreme, even excessive, ingenuity, but if that ingenuity leads to the kind of destructiveness that man has been practicing in the recent period, man's ingenuity may yet prove itself to have been the most selectively disadvantageous trait that any creature has yet developed.

Man prides himself upon the variety of his inventiveness, but the variety of animated nature is far greater than that achieved by man. If man would simply have the grace and the humility to acknowledge himself the made-over ape that he is, he might be able to see the world of which he is a part in truer perspective. Like most self-made men, man, who has made himself, is an outstanding example of unskilled labor, a very imperfect creature, indeed. Man is, in fact, the only example of 150-pound nonlinear servomechanism that can be wholly reproduced by unskilled labor—and the lack of skill he exhibits in the making of human beings is prodigious. Indeed, that lack of skill theatens to put an end to us all. What man has made of man and of the world in which he lives is a sorry story. What animal, indeed, has created as much devastation? It is written in the Book of Job:

Ask now the beasts and they shall teach thee; and the fowls of the air, and they shall teach thee:

Or speak to the earth, and it shall teach thee and the fishes of the sea shall declare unto thee.

Who knoweth not in all these that the hand of the Lord hath wrought this? In whose hand is the soul of every living thing, and the breath of all mankind.

And in the Koran it is written,

There is no beast on earth nor fowl that flieth, but the same are a people like unto you, and to God they shall return.

Without accepting these words in their literal sense, the fundamental truths they express are beyond dispute, namely, that we can learn from these other "peoples," and that we ought to love and respect them for what they are, our kin.

Who but a few have ever given any attention to the profound meaning of those words? Saint Francis of Assisi, whose love for all living creatures is a part of our tradition, is regarded as an eccentric who carried things too far, and to whom, at best, we offer up the smoke of incense as before an empty shrine.

Man may yet restore himself to health if he will learn to understand himself in relation to the world of nature in which he evolved as an integral part, and to appreciate the nature of his relationship to the world of nature. He has for too long diminished himself by his prejudiced and false views of himself in relation to that nature, and in so doing he has diminished and devastated so much of the rest of the world. He has everything to gain from taking a fresh look at the world of nature and making it a part of life as essential to him as he is essential to it. The lessons man may learn from the study of nature are of at least as great significance as any he can learn from the purely human tradition, for as Wordsworth said in the poem already quoted:

> *Nature never did betray*
> *The heart that loved her; 'tis her privilege*
> *Through all the years of this our life, to lead*
> *From joy to joy: for she can so inform the mind*
> *The mind that is within us, so impress*
> *With quietness and beauty, and so feed*
> *With lofty thoughts, that neither evil tongues,*
> *Rash judgments, nor the sneers of selfish men,*
> *Nor greetings where no kindness is, nor all*
> *The dreary intercourses of daily life,*
> *Shall e'er prevail against us, or disturb*
> *Our cheerful faith that all which we behold*
> *Is full of blessings.*

WILDERNESS—A PSYCHIATRIC NECESSITY

≫ *William C. Gibson*

Much has been spoken and written on the "how" of wilderness areas and national parks, their acquisition, management, and protection. Today I want to say something about the "why" of wilderness areas, since it seems to me that this question is primary. It is vital to any wise program, and it is essential if public support for these areas is to be kindled. Millions of users of public parklands cannot be rallied to arms if the advocates of wilderness areas spend very much time bickering among themselves over problems to which there are, as yet, no scientific answers. If we truly believe that the last chance to appeal to the conscience of America on this subject is at hand, we should concentrate on the positive human values which national parks and wilderness areas offer to society. There is no doubt in my mind, as a psychiatrist, about these positive medical values. The parks of London were once called "the lungs of the people." Today, we should be shouting from the rooftops that the parklands of America are the greatest mental health guardians we have.

I want to start with a consideration of a recent statement by Sir Julian Huxley:

If man is responsible for the future of this planet, he must pay more attention to ecology—the science of relations between organisms and the resources of their environment.

Human ecology involves finding out what resources are available in our environment and how to make the best use of them. We have to think first of all the material resources—minerals, water power, soil, forests, agricultural production—but we must also think of the non-material or enjoyment resources of the habitat, such as natural beauty and solitude, interest and adventure, wild scenery and wildlife.

We should set about planning a Fulfillment Society—rather than a Welfare Society, an Efficiency Society, or a Power Society.

I don't think Huxley is merely voicing an opinion. He is stating a fact. And the fact is that any resource development that tramples on the human factor in our society is in for trouble—sooner or later. In the days of Henry the Eighth, it was possible for a group of pirates to "enclose" the public lands known as "commons" for their private sheep farming. Henry symbolizes what his countryman Wilfred Trotter later called "the beefy fist and the mutton mind."

Let me condense the remarkable story of private versus public interest in developing the open lands in Britain. Just a century ago the British Parliament brought to a halt the system of the land buccaneers like Henry the Eighth, a system which in its 150 years of operation cost the people of England one acre out of every seven. In their time, Bishop Latimer and Sir Thomas More fought against the iniquity, but without success. When, however, the great cities of the Industrial Revolution began to develop, they required psychiatric safety valves in the forms of parks—in fact anything reminiscent of Mother Nature in the stark surroundings of the factory era. In 1865 an attempt was made to enclose Wimbledon Common and Epsom Common. The populace of London rebelled. A young Member of Parliament, Henry Fawcett, professor of political economy at Cambridge, called for a Select Committee to investigate the problem as it applied to all large industrial cities. It became evident that the survival of industrial Britain was at stake, and that the toiling mass of humanity on whose back it depended were going to need all the local commons and more.

Epping Forest became the prize in a momentous legal battle between the Corporation of the City of London and fourteen "lords of manors" who sought to subdivide the forest, just as they sought to subdivide vast holdings in London. The City Corporation won the suit, and today thousands upon thousands of Londoners and their neighbors can be seen picnicking in Epping Forest.

One wonders why Fawcett won the battle which Latimer and More had waged but lost. Unquestionably the time was right, but more than this, Fawcett was the right man at this right time. A lawyer, trained at Cambridge and Lincoln's Inn, he was blinded at the age of 25 in a hunting accident. This did not stop him fishing, rowing, skating, and riding. The recreations which he enjoyed as the son of a very successful business family of Salisbury, he was determined would be brought within the reach of all. He was a member of one of those radical, yet conservative families, that have forced us to preserve our resources, recreational and mental, with precious little help or understanding from the public at first. The Act of 1876 permanently placed the public interest before any private one concerning "open spaces" in Britain. The Ministers of Agriculture and Health have to be satisfied that in any future development, the public interest is being protected. Since 1925 the law in Britain has given "to the public a statutory right of access for air and exercise on every common or place of manorial waste and to any rural common."

Every time we go to the post office and use parcel post, or buy postal money orders, or consult the little sign as to the time of the next collection, let us remember Henry Fawcett, pioneer in land resource development, for it was Fawcett who, as Gladstone's Postmaster General, introduced these innovations also. Clearly, we need more Henry Fawcetts.

The French Revolution threw up some remarkable men, one of the most notorious being Jean Paul Marat, sometime physician, lawyer, and thief. Visiting Oxford, he was attracted to a famous collection of gold coins in the Ashmolean Museum. He gained the confidence of a professor who loaned him the keys to the Museum, no doubt as his contribution to biculturalism. Marat made off with the old coins on Saturday and was on Monday apprehended in Bristol. Brought back to Oxford to stand trial, Marat was quick to acknowledge that to steal from a person was a crime punishable by death. But, he contended, to steal from a public body was no crime at all. As history records, he survived long enough to be stabbed to death in his bath by Charlotte Corday, in Paris, a fitting fate for those who believe in legalized public plunder.

So much for history. What of the future? It seems to me that everyone is talking about the population explosion, while no one is talking about the need for a parks explosion. As a matter of fact the parks explosion will have to exceed the population explosion for two very good reasons: (a) the fraction of our population over age sixty-five grows daily higher; (b) the work week is likely to be 35 hours by 1970.

Little wonder that Ontario's Minister of Labor, the Honorable Leslie Rowntree, predicts that "one of the big preoccupations of governments during the next generation will be the necessary increase in parklands and in recreational programs to help the public use more leisure more effectively."

As a psychiatrist, I am appalled at the lack of public knowledge of the positive value of recreation. It is strange that while we annually debate its merits, modern mental hospitals use it daily to help rehabilitate patients. Obviously it should not be necessary to enter a mental hospital in order to gain access to a good recreational program, and yet there is a grain of truth in all this. Conversely, one wonders if a sound recreational program might not reduce the number entering mental hospitals.

Along with scientific research into causes of these expensive diseases, I am convinced that recreation will eventually be seen as a wise investment in human resources. It has been estimated here in the United States that every time we make unnecessary the admission of a patient to a mental hospital we save the taxpayer an immediate $5,600. When I tell you that this country has as many mental hospital beds as general hospital beds, you will appreciate the size of the financial stakes involved. The losses to industry, through absenteeism of mental origin, are enormous. Recreation, parklands, and do-it-yourself sports offer great savings in terms of dollars and of lives in the year 1965.

Let me conclude with the words of Britain's great historian, George Trevelyan, O.M., one of the moving spirits in the National Trust:

... the need to preserve natural beauty, ... is not merely a question of preserving holiday grounds for masses of people from the town. It is also a matter of preserving a main source of spiritual well being and inspiration, on which our ancestors throve and which we are in danger of losing forever. The two objects indeed are hardly to be distinguished. For the value of the holiday ground as such depends not merely on supplying air and exercise to the city worker, but on offering him the spiritual delight and sustenance that he cannot get in the modern city, so completely divorced from nature. We are literally 'children of the earth,' and removed from her, our spirit withers or runs to various forms of insanity. Unless we can refresh ourselves at least by intermittent contact with nature, we grow awry.

This flag of beauty, hung out by the mysterious universe, to claim the worship of the heart of man, what is it, and what does its signal mean to us? There is no clear interpretation. But that does not lessen its value. Like the universe, like life, natural beauty also is a mystery. But whatever it may be, whether casual in its origin as some hold who love it well, or whether, as others hold, such splendour can be nothing less than the purposeful message of God—whatever its interpretation may be, natural beauty is the ultimate spiritual appeal of the universe, of nature, or of the God of nature, to their nursling man. It and it alone makes a common appeal to the sectaries of all our religious and scientific creeds, to the lovers of all our different schools of poetry and art, ancient and modern, and to many more beside these. It is the highest common denominator in the spiritual life of today.

Yet now that it is most consciously valued, it is being most rapidly destroyed upon this planet, and above all in this island. In old days it needed no conservation. Man was camped in the midst of it and could not get outside it, still less destroy it. Indeed, until the end of the eighteenth century the works of man only added to the beauty of nature. But science and machinery have now armed him with weapons that will be his own making or undoing, as he chooses to use them; at present he is destroying natural beauty space in the ordinary course of business and economy. Therefore, unless he now will be at pains to make rules for the preservation of natural beauty, unless he consciously protects it at the partial expense of some of his other greedy activities, he will cut off his own spiritual supplies, and leave his descendants a helpless prey forever to the base materialism of mean and vulgar sights.

This matter has become a public question of the first magnitude. The value of natural beauty is admitted in words by our public men, but when it comes to deeds, the doctrine is too new to bear much fruit. It has for centuries been held sacrilege to destroy a church. But a place of natural beauty may be destroyed, and is often so taxed by the State that it must be sold to the jerry-builder. Meanwhile, the State itself pours forth the money of taxpayer and ratepayer for the perpetration all over the island of outrages on the beauty of the country. Those who mourn over the destruction of abbeys long ago, should look also at the beam in our own eye, and hasten to save from destruction or disfigurement parks, woodlands, and valley heads.

This is a civic duty that cannot any longer be neglected without dire consequences. Destruction walks by noonday. Unless the State reverses the engines and instead of speeding up destruction, plans the development of the country so that the minimum of harm can be done to beauty, the future of our race, whatever its social, economical, and political structure may be, will be brutish and shorn of spiritual value.

So says Trevelyan, and I am sure this afternoon so say we all here.

FACETS OF WILDERNESS

⇶ *Margaret W. Owings*

These two days we have been turning over in our hands a great rough rock with many facets. It is a treasured rock. We call it "wilderness." Each facet is one variety of this wilderness, and the reflection from each facet is a human response to that experience.

There are those of us who look at wilderness primarily as a dimension—an immensity, a grand proportion—the horizon large in outline against the dark mountain range. These may be people who work by expansion and think by expansion, fanning out their interests. It's the broad, deep picture they find rewarding.

Then, there are those who turn primarily to the intimate savor of landscape: the detail, the scent of nettle and mint, the lazy buzz of a mountain fly, the careless grace of a flower opening. These people are selective and concentrate their attention, finding their reward in infinite detail.

But neither approach seeks confinement. Both pursue the sense of the unexplored landscape. For each man is his own eager explorer.

It was Rachel Carson who unrolled the long vistas before our eyes and defined man's place as a mere moment of time. "This particular moment of time that is mine," she repeated again and again to help us see our place and our role and the perils of our future in the long view.

It is the perceptive explorer who can glimpse this view, who can uncover the links and bridges of history and find his own particular place in the moment of time.

Having a landscape to oneself is a singular pleasure. Many of us stumble upon this by surprise. Suddenly it is there—unshared, solitary. One may well experience a reckless moment of freedom, a penetrating moment of understanding. A meaning that was elusive is suddenly clear! And in the words of Freya Stark, one can carry long afterwards "a secret sense of exile."

Promise is a word I associate with wilderness. Promise and independence are rare qualities found deep in solitude. Promise renews faith. Independence is found only when the sense of belonging is understood.

Sigurd Olson spoke of "the animal oneness with the earth," the sense of close relationship, of belonging.

How can we recapture this relationship?

How can we return to this "oneness"?

What kind of a ceremony can lead us back: The Mountain Chant of the Navajos in their dark circle of branches? The Hopi Snake dancers at Walpi, stamping on the Sapupai—the door to the inner earth?

Sigurd Olson quoted Pierre Teilhard de Chardin (that rare soul who could make an experience flare with a presence) as saying that only if man is receptive, contemplative, and aware can he open these doors to what the universe and life really mean—can he open these doors to belonging. But for most of us, under the pressures and conflicts of human society, it is only in the setting of wilderness that this revelation can unfold.

I, myself, experienced a form of revelation one autumn morning. In an unexpected moment, I witnessed a thin slice of wilderness, fleeting and brief, but filled with a meaning somehow intensified by the counterpart of its setting.

I was on the sidewalk of 55th Street in the heart of New York City. Around me was the noise and confusion, the frantic strain of traffic, horns and whistles. Tall buildings cast their shadows over the deep chasm of the street. It was the essence of the man-made world.

At that moment, as if by signal, every city sound about me was suddenly hushed. All mechanical uproar was arrested abruptly, as if the power had been shut off. And in the silence of that instant, I heard but one thing—the delicate honking of geese high overhead. I looked up through the slot of buildings to another dimension, as a V of geese moved south, calling to one another as they passed out of view.

One world gave away to another.

It was one of those "burning instances of truth," referred to by Sigurd Olson, "when everything stands clear."

Now Loren Eiseley admonishes emissaries returning from wilderness to record their marvel, not to define its meaning. But I am tempted to call your attention to several potent words used by Sigurd Olson: timelessness, majestic rhythms.

Each of you alone can read your own symbols into the incident I have tried to describe. But it seems appropriate, with the dedication of the Dag Hammarskjold Memorial Grove, to close with these lines from his diary.

A wind from my unknown goal
Stirs the strings
In expectation.
Shall I ever get there?
There, where life resounds
A clear pure note—
In the silence.

SUMMARY OF THE CONFERENCE

➻ *Harold Gilliam*

This Wilderness Conference has been a disillusioning experience—disillusioning in the literal sense. Rather than dealing in the usual conference clichés, speaker after speaker punctured popular illusions, shattered whole batteries of common assumptions, and laid to rest battalions of myths, including these:

The myth that the need for park and wilderness areas increases at the same rate as the population.

Actually it increases about four times as fast as the population, owing to increased leisure, higher incomes, and the growing popularity of outdoor recreation. (Lincoln H. Day)

The myth that the U. S. population explosion, which threatens to leave Standing Room Only in parks and wilderness areas, can be controlled by handing out birth control information.

"Our rapid population increase derives hardly at all from unwanted children. It comes, instead, from those third, fourth, fifth children whose parents want them. . . . It is motivation, not techniques, that is the key to population control.

"What we must work toward is a society . . . in which couples limited their families to but two children because that was the accepted pattern of behavior." (Lincoln H. Day)

The myth that the wilderness is of use only to the rugged few.

Wilderness areas are of immeasurable value to science as natural laboratories where man can learn from nature the lessons necessary to his own survival. (Albert E. Burke)

And access to nature is essential to everyone's mental health in an age of increasing urban tension. "We should be shouting from the rooftops that the parklands of America are the greatest mental health guardians we have." (William C. Gibson)

The myth that it is possible to save the wilderness by saving wilderness.

Population pressures will wipe out the wilderness unless we also provide a whole range of alternative recreation areas, from city and regional parks to such vast playgrounds as Northern California's new 250,000-acre Whiskeytown-Shasta-Trinity National Recreation Area. (James K. Carr)

The myth that wilderness can be preserved by leaving it alone.

In some cases it may be necessary to counteract the effects of man's past activities by actively restoring the natural balance, as in the National Park Service's program to reduce Yellowstone's overpopulation of elk. (George Hartzog)

The myth that engineers can calculate what's best for everybody.

Engineers justify dams and highways in wilderness areas (and elsewhere) by elaborately calculated "cost-benefit ratios," showing that the dollar benefit is greater than the dollar cost. These calculations are gobbledygook. They do not include non-monetary values, and even in adding up the dollars and cents, the engineers can select the figures that will justify what they have already decided to do.

Yet these kinds of calculations are being used to justify freeways through the redwoods and destructive dams in the Grand Canyon and on the Yukon.

Glen Canyon Dam on the upper Colorado has already destroyed some of the most spectacular river landscapes on the continent, just as San Francisco's Hetch Hetchy Dam long ago wiped out the valley that was a twin to Yosemite, because costs were reckoned on the narrow engineering basis.

The engineers fail to calculate what may be the greatest value of all—the value of natural beauty left alone. "The emphasis on least cost as it is presently interpreted does not provide society with an adequate choice." And it reduces "flexibility of choice left for future generations." (Luna Leopold)

"We do not have to believe what the engineers tell us about highway construction costs and benefits. The fact is that they can calculate the cost of the concrete and the saving on automobile wear and tear. They cannot calculate the far more important cost of destroying the wilderness and therefore they ignore it . . .

"What right have they to decide what weight ought to be given our social life, environment, political organization, esthetics, recreation, pleasures, scenic view and other intangibles?" (J. B. Condliffe)

The myth that dams on our rivers are necessary to produce essential power.

"The preservation of a river as a thing of beauty, rather than as a dam site, hastens but infinitesimally the time which must inevitably come in any case, the time at which all power will be derived from nuclear energy." (James Bonner)

The myth that conservationists are fighting inevitably losing battles against the bulldozers.

If the conservation movement continues to grow, it is conceivable that it may become one of the leading political coalitions in the country and the "wildlife vote" may one day become as important to politicians as the farm vote, the business vote and the labor vote.

Conservationists might well make common cause with the anti-poverty and civil rights movements and convince potential political allies that they are "concerned not merely with plants and animals but with the integrity of life as a whole." (Albert Lepawsky)

A word or two of my own in conclusion, following up on the statement of Trevelyan which was quoted by Dr. Gibson, about the fact that natural beauty is being taxed out of existence. This is particularly true here in the San Francisco Bay Area.

For example, the farmers in the Santa Clara Valley, because they are in the midst of a growing suburban area, are taxed as though their land were urban land, valued several times more than what their land is worth as farmland. The farms are literally being taxed out of existence. Scenic open space in other areas is being taxed out of existence. I know people who own small redwood groves and who would like to keep them. But the tax on the redwoods is so great—because the assessor regards them as standing timber—that the owners are forced to log the trees or sell out and the redwoods are lost.

I would suggest that if open space can be taxed out of existence, possibly it can be taxed back into existence—or at least it can be taxed so that it will remain in existence. There are many precedents for tax exemptions, for religious groups, educational groups, charitable groups. If we recognize that it is public policy to maintain open space, why should we not give tax exemptions to the owners of open space as well?

There is an answer to that. Public officials throw up their hands and say, "We can't exempt everybody; we need the money." This is particularly true in the areas around growing cities, where large amounts of money are necessary to build new schools, roads, libraries and sewers. Local governments need more tax revenue, not less.

In the counties around the northern part of San Francisco Bay, which have more open space and are less developed than the counties to the south, the county governments can't afford to do the things they should do to maintain the open space, because they don't have industry, which is a major source of tax revenue. They are trying to attract more industry to get an adequate tax base. But factories use up the valuable open space we are trying to preserve.

I think that in many of these areas the greatest asset is their scenery, and the best industry could be the tourist trade—visitors who will come into the areas to see the scenery. To replace their orchards and vineyards with factories may be to destroy their most productive assets.

They could collect more in taxes on land without penalizing owners of open space and without attracting factories. I'm talking about taxes on land speculation. There are millions of dollars made by speculators who buy land and later sell it for two, three, five, or ten times what they paid for it. They may have done nothing to improve it. Every cent of the increased value may have been due to social causes, the population moving around that area. In these cases the property owner is not responsible for the increase in value. The community was responsible for this increase in value, so why should not the community benefit from this increase? Why not tax the land speculator? Why not claim for community purposes the increased value created by community activities? Higher taxes on profits from land speculation would go a long ways toward paying for more parks and scenic easements and permitting tax exemptions for owners of open space without attracting factories that destroy scenic values.

Perhaps it is time for conservationists to make themselves experts in such fields as taxation, local government, and practical politics. Possibly we should all follow the advice of the first great conservationist and politician and lobbyist, John Muir, who wrote in a letter to a friend during the Hetch-Hetchy fight, "I'm now an experienced lobbyist. My political education is complete. I have attended the legislature, made speeches, explained, exhorted, persuaded every mother's son of the legislators, newspaper reporters, and everybody else who would listen to me."

In the best tradition of John Muir, the California Roadside Council has pioneered in the establishment of an organization, the Planning and Conservation League for Legislative Action, which is planning to hire a full-time representative in Sacramento to lobby for conservation causes. This is something we can all get behind. When we get tired of political activity, we can renew our energies by following an even more famous piece of advice from John Muir. "Climb the mountains and get their good tidings. Nature's peace will flow into you as sunshine flows into trees. The winds will blow their own freshness into you and the storms their energy, while cares will drop off like autumn leaves."

The first part of the summary above is Mr. Gilliam's condensation of his original conference presentation. It was published in the *San Francisco Chronicle* for April 11, 1965, and was reprinted in the April 1965 *Sierra Club Bulletin.*

BIOGRAPHICAL NOTES

CLINTON P. ANDERSON has been United States Senator from New Mexico since 1948. Prior to this he served as Secretary of Agriculture in the cabinet of President Truman and was a Representative at Large for New Mexico in the 77th, 78th, and 79th Congresses. He was Treasurer of New Mexico in 1933 and 1934. He also worked in the insurance business and as a newspaperman. Senator Anderson has been directly involved in the passage of much Federal legislation to preserve our natural resource heritage and has served as chairman of the Senate Committee on Interior and Insular Affairs. He was one of the principal architects of the Wilderness Act and worked closely with the late Howard Zahniser of The Wilderness Society who first presented the idea of a Wilderness Bill at the 1951 Wilderness Conference. He is now chairman of the Senate Committee on Aeronautical and Space Sciences.

JAMES BONNER, professor of biology at the California Institute of Technology, received his bachelor's degree from the University of Utah and his Ph.D. from the California Institute of Technology. His work has been entirely in the field of experimental biology, principally in recent years in relation to the molecular basis of development and differentiation. In addition, however, he has taken a lively interest in the future of our industrial culture and in the future of the outdoors and of wilderness. He is co-author with Harrison Brown and John Weir of an exploration of our future, *The Next Hundred Years*. He has traveled to, and lectured in, many parts of the world—Europe, Asia, Africa, Oceania. He is a devoted mountaineer and skier, a member of the American Alpine Club, the National Ski Patrol system, and a past chairman of the Sierra Club Rock Climbing section and a member of the club's Desert Peaks and Hundred Peaks sections.

PAUL BROOKS, author of *Roadless Area,* is almost as well known among conservationists as he is as editor-in-chief of Houghton Mifflin Company, the distinguished Boston publishers. He was graduated in 1931 from Harvard College, where he is a member of Phi Beta Kappa. Formerly a director of the Massachusetts Audubon Society, he is vice president of Trustees for Conservation, a member of the National Council of the Nature Conservancy, and was a participant in the First World Conference on National Parks in Seattle in July, 1962. He is a fellow of the American Academy of Arts and Sciences. He lives in Lincoln, Massachusetts, where he takes an active part in local conservation.

DAVID BROWER, executive director of the Sierra Club since 1952, joined the club in 1933, went on its editorial board in 1935, and in his twenties made a notable climbing and ski-mountaineering record. In 1939 he began participating in the club's wilderness outing program initiated by John Muir and William E. Colby, and led two thousand members on wilderness outings. He joined the staff during the Kings Canyon Park battle, was elected a director of the club, then went to the University of California Press as editor, concurrently producing and editing club books and films. A Combat Infantryman with the Mountain Troops, he helped mountain train five divisions, and retired a major in the Reserve. He was chairman of the Natural Resources Council, and is secretary of Trustees for Conservation. He edited the *Sierra Club Bulletin* from 1946 to 1953 and has served as editor of the Exhibit Format Series, winner of the Carey-Thomas award in 1964.

ALBERT E. BURKE received his B.A. and M.A. from the University of California (UCLA) and his Ph.D. in International Relations (International Aspects of Resource Use) from the University of Pennsylvania. He held the post of director of graduate studies in conservation and resource use at Yale University from 1951 to 1957. He is a former director of the American Institute of Resource Economics and former consultant in industrial development for the Connecticut Light and Power Company on natural resources and conservation. He and his wife have spent considerable time working and living with the American Indians on reservations in the southwestern part of the United States. For two years he lived in Soviet Russia and has spent periods of time in Germany and Czechoslovakia as well as in the Far East. He is considered an authority in the field of conservation as well as in the fields of geography, geopolitics, and world affairs.

In 1957 Dr. Burke was appointed educational television consultant for the National Broadcasting Company where he produced the award-winning series "Survival."

JAMES K. CARR, general manager of public utilities for the City and County of San Francisco, served as Under Secretary of the Interior from 1961 to 1964. Prior to this he served as assistant general manager of the Sacramento Municipal Utility District, as consultant to the Committee on Interior and Insular Affairs of the House of Representatives, and in various capacities with the Bureau of Reclamation of the Department of the Interior. He twice served as chairman of an international engineering and scientific panel on use of nuclear power to promote desalinization of sea water. He is a registered professional engineer and a fellow of the American Society of Civil Engineers.

JOHN A. CARVER, JR., Under Secretary of the Interior, was formerly the Assistant Secretary of the Interior for Public Land Management. He received his A.B. degree from Brigham Young University and his LL.B. from Georgetown University, following which he practiced law in Idaho, including service as Assistant Attorney General of Idaho. From 1957–1961, he served as administrative assistant to Senator Frank Church of Idaho.

EDWARD P. CLIFF, a graduate of Utah State University, has been chief of the Forest Service, U.S. Department of Agriculture, since March 1962. He rose to that position after 31 years' experience on National Forest assignments in the Pacific Northwest, the Intermountain and Central Rocky Mountain Regions, and the Washington office. For 10 years before becoming chief he was assistant chief in charge of National Forest Administration. Since playing a leading personal role in the moves leading to the creation of the Kalmiopsis Wild Area, he has been very close to the country's wilderness movement and for the past decade has played a key personal role in the designation of all National Forest wilderness-type areas and in the management of National Forest areas and uses of all kinds. He was the chairman of the U.S. Board of Geographic Names from 1961–1965 and of the North American Forestry Commission (FAO) from 1963–1965. In 1962 the Department of Agriculture conferred on him its highest recognition: its Distinguished Service Award "for consistently outstanding vision, courage, and dedicated leadership in developing, administering, and managing the resources of the National Forest System in an age of conflicting interests and dynamic change."

JOHN B. CONDLIFFE joined Stanford Research Institute in 1959 where his present position is senior economist, industrial and development economics. He has held chairs of economics in Canterbury, Michigan, London, Yale, and California. In between his teaching appointments he wrote the first six World Economic Surveys for the League of Nations (for which Yale University later gave him the Henry E. Howland Memorial Prize). He has acted as rapporteur-general for the International Chamber of Commerce and rapporteur for the International Studies Conference. Dr. Condliffe took his first degrees, M.A. and D.Sc. (Economics), at the University of New Zealand, and has since been given an honorary LL.D. by Occidental College and D.Litt. by the University of New Zealand.

He has written many books and articles on international economic questions. In 1950, *The Commerce of Nations* was awarded the Wendell Willkie Prize by the American Political Science Association. Dr. Condliffe is a life member of the Royal Economic Society, a fellow of the American Association for the Advancement of Science, an honorary Phi Beta Kappa, a member of the American Economic Association, past president of the Western Economic Association, and a foundation member of the Economic Society of Australia and New Zealand.

EDWARD C. CRAFTS is the first director of the new Bureau of Outdoor Recreation of the Department of the Interior. Prior to this appointment in 1962, he had served for 12 years as assistant chief of the U.S. Forest Service, Department of Agriculture. As a graduate forester with B.F., M.F., and Ph.D. degrees from the University of Michigan, he had earlier undertaken assignments with U.S. Forest and Range Experiment Stations in Ogden, Utah, Tucson, Arizona, and Berkeley, California. He served as chief of the Division of Forest Economics, U.S. Forest Service from 1944–1950. Dr. Crafts is author of *Timber Resources for America's Future*.

LINCOLN H. DAY is an associate professor of sociology and public health at Yale University. Just prior to his present position, he was a research associate at Harvard's School of Public Health and served as a member of the associate staff of medicine, Harvard School of Medicine. He received his B.A. from Yale University and his M.A. and Ph.D. in sociology from Columbia University. In addition to his present post, he has taught sociology at Mount Holyoke College and Princeton University, and served as research associate, Bureau of Applied Social Research, Columbia University, and visiting fellow in demography at the Australian National University. He has written about a dozen professional articles on population and a book, *Disabled Workers in the Labor Market* (with A. J. Jaffe and Walter Adams). He is co-author with his wife, Alice Taylor Day, of *Too Many Americans,* a book concerned with the current population situation in the United States.

WILLIAM C. GIBSON, professor of neurological research at the University of British Columbia, is interested not only in medicine, specifically neurology and psychiatry, but also in the history of medicine and in natural resources. He received his undergraduate training at the University of British Columbia and then studied medicine at McGill University and physiology at Oxford University. Dr. Gibson joined the medical research branch of the Royal Canadian Air Force and worked in the area of high altitude physiology and problems of motion sickness. He has been an officer in the Natural Resource Conference in Canada and the president of the Save Our Parklands Association of Vancouver.

HAROLD GILLIAM is a columnist for the *San Francisco Chronicle* and the author of several books on San Francisco, the most recent being *The Face of San Francisco* in collaboration with Phil Palmer. He is also author of the Sierra Club's *Island in Time: The Point Reyes Peninsula.* Mr. Gilliam served as an assistant to the Secretary of the Interior from 1962–1963. He teaches in the extension division of San Francisco State College and is active in civic affairs of the Bay region. He is especially concerned with the preservation of open space and with sound urban planning.

JAMES P. GILLIGAN, extension forester, University of California, Berkeley, received his B.S. in Forestry, his M.S. and Ph.D. from the University of Michigan. From 1946 to 1950 he served as instructor in forestry and zoology at Boise Junior College, Boise, Idaho. He was professor of forestry, Oklahoma State University, from 1953 to 1956. In 1958, he became chairman of the recreation division, Society of

American Foresters, in 1960, chairman of the Society's Forest Wild-life Division, and in 1962 chairman of its Bay Area Section.

He was appointed consultant to the President's Outdoor Recreation Resources Review Commission in 1961, and served in 1961–1962 as Director of the ORRRC study on "Wilderness and Recreation" by the University of California Wildland Research Center. Since 1948 he has written thirty publications on wilderness, outdoor recreation, forestry and forest land management.

ARIE J. HAAGEN-SMIT has been professor in bio-organic chemistry at California Institute of Technology since 1937. He was born in Utrecht, Holland, and studied at the University of Utrecht where he obtained a Ph.D. in 1929. During recent years he has applied himself to the chemical identification of the irritants present in the air around Los Angeles and the Bay Area. This led to the discovery of the causes of Los Angeles smog. It was recognized that petroleum products and nitrogen oxides can be dangerous air pollutants, not because of their individual toxicities, but because they may react among themselves to form irritating intermediate products. Dr. Haagen-Smit has received many honors in connection with his research in bio-organic chemistry and air pollution control. In 1950 he won the ACS Fritzsche Award for his research on essential oils and flavors. His work on air pollutants won him an award from the Air Pollution Control Association in 1958. Dr. Haagen-Smit has presented papers and participated in air pollution symposia throughout the country. As a member of the Pollution Panel of the President's Scientific Advisory Committee, his duties include the promotion of sound and legal ways in the proper use and conservation of air, water, and soil.

GEORGE B. HARTZOG, JR., director of the National Park Service since 1964, has served the Park Service since 1946 as an attorney and as assistant superintendent of Rocky Mountain and Great Smoky Mountains national parks prior to his promotion in 1959 to superintendent of Jefferson National Expansion Memorial in St. Louis, Missouri. Before joining the Service, Mr. Hartzog was employed as adjudicator in the Bureau of Land Management. In 1956 he received the Meritorious Award Certificate from William A. Jump Memorial Foundation and, in 1962, the Department of the Interior's Distinguished Service Award.

CLARK KERR served with the War Labor Board from 1943–1945, at which time he joined the Institute of Industrial Relations at the University of California in Berkeley, serving as its director until 1952. He was then appointed chancellor of the Berkeley campus of the University and served until 1958 when he was appointed president of all the many campuses of the University of California, the position he now holds. He is also professor of industrial relations and business administration in the Department of Economics. He received his B.A. degree from Swarthmore College, his M.A. degree from Stanford, and his Ph.D. degree from the University of California. He has been awarded numerous honorary degrees from institutions in America and abroad. He is author of a number of publications including *Unions, Management, and the Public* (with E. Wight Bakke), *Industrialism and Industrial Man* (with Dunlop, Harbison, and Myers), and *The Uses of the University.*

CHAUNCEY D. LEAKE, pharmacologist, author, historian, and a past president of the American Association for the Advancement of Science, has taught at the University of Wisconsin and the University of California, was executive vice president in charge of the medical branch of the University of Texas from 1942 to 1955, and was professor of pharmacology at Ohio State University. His works include *Letheon, Can We Agree? Old Egyptian Medicine, Ashbel Smith and Yellow Fever, Some Founders of Physiology,* and *The Amphetamines.* He also translated Harvey's *De Motu Cordis.* He is now at the University of California Medical School in San Francisco.

LUNA B. LEOPOLD, chief hydrologist for the U.S. Geological Survey for ten years, relinquished his administrative duties in 1966 and is now research hydrologist. His experience in the engineering field covers many aspects of water-resources development, particularly in hydrology. Much of his time in recent years has been devoted to research in the field of river mechanics, the hydrologic and physiographic characteristics of river channels, and on certain aspects of water-sediment relations in rivers. Though geomorphology—especially river mechanics and sediment movement—has been his primary concern in recent years, his research has included a variety of studies in climatology, soils, and hydrology. The subject to which he has devoted particular attention is gully erosion in the southwestern United States.

Dr. Leopold has worked with several governmental agencies dealing with water in New Mexico and Arizona and in Washington, D.C. He is author (with Thomas Maddock, Jr.) of *The Flood Control*

Controversy, 1954, a book on flood control policy in the U.S., and (with M. G. Wolman and John P. Miller) of *Fluvial Processes in Geomorphology,* as well as author of many scientific papers. He is recipient of the Kirk Bryan Award of the Geological Society of America and the Veth Medal of the Royal Netherlands Geographical Society, and the Distinguished Service Award of the U.S. Department of the Interior.

ALBERT LEPAWSKY, professor of political science at the University of California since 1953, has served as a consultant to the U.S. Natural Resources Board, 1935–1941, as a member of the Chicago Planning Commission, 1940–1942, and as a consultant to local, state, national and international agencies since 1940. He was a member of the UN Mission of Technical Assistance to Bolivia in 1950–1951. Professor Lepawsky served as president of the California Conservation Council from 1958–1960, and as chairman of the steering committee of a Seminar on Development and Administration of the International River Basin, at the Regional Training Center for UN Fellows at Vancouver, Canada, in September 1961. He was secretary of the Bay Area Chapter, Society for International Development, in 1963, and served as president of the Western Political Science Association in 1964.

ASHLEY MONTAGU, anthropologist, social biologist, and author, served as chairman of the Department of Anthropology at Rutgers University from 1949–1955. He was appointed Regents Professor at the University of California at Santa Barbara in 1962. He has held numerous posts relating to his interests in anthropology and problems of race, including family affairs editor and anthropology advisor for NBC-TV (1954); rapporteur responsible for drafting statement on race for UNESCO, 1949–1950; and expert witness on legal and scientific problems relating to race since 1930. Among his many books are *On Being Human* (1950), *Statement on Race* (1952), and *The Humanization of Man* (1962).

SIGURD F. OLSON is a consultant on natural areas and wilderness preservation to the Secretary of the Interior, the director of the National Park Service, the President's Quetico-Superior Committee, and the Izaak Walton League of America. He is vice president of the Wilderness Society, a past president of the National Parks Association, and a member of the Sierra Club and many other conservation groups. In his early years he was a guide in the Quetico-Superior country of Minnesota and Canada and has since not only seen most of the wilderness of the United States but has followed the great rivers and chains of lakes from the U.S. border to the Arctic Coast and Hudson Bay. His writings include many magazine articles, and such books as *The Singing Wilderness, Listening Point, The Lonely Land,* and *Runes of the North,* accounts of expeditions and interpretive essays on the meaning of wilderness.

MARGARET WENTWORTH OWINGS is a native Californian, an artist, and a graduate of Mills College. Her interest in conservation work began after the war when she helped the Point Lobos League in Carmel, California, preserve beaches in the Monterey area. She led the campaign to protect the sea-lions along the California coast from legislative action, which could have resulted in their being killed in large numbers and organized a campaign that resulted in the removal of the California bounty on mountain lions. For her work in this latter campaign, she received a special citation from the National Audubon Society. In 1963 she was appointed to the California State Park Commission, a post she still holds. In this capacity she has been active in efforts to protect California's Redwood State Parks from damaging freeway routings.

T. ERIC REYNOLDS, M.D., has served as president of the California Conservation Council, the Golden Gate Audubon Society, and the Cooper Ornithological Society. He is also a member of the Board of Governors of the City of Oakland Cultural Foundation. He is a graduate of the University of California and its Medical School and has been in private practice in Oakland since 1926, in the course of which time he has become one of California's most eminent physicians and conservationists.

PAUL B. SEARS, eminent American botanist and conservationist, was chairman of the Conservation Program at Yale, where in 1950 he had established one of the first graduate programs of research and instruction in conservation of natural resources, and from which he retired in June, 1960. A past president of the American Association for the Advancement of Science, the Ecological Society of America, and the American Society of Naturalists, and a former chairman of the board of the National Audubon Society, his special field of interest is ecology, its application in the management of natural resources and in the history of vegetation.

He received his B.S. from Ohio Wesleyan, his M.A. from Nebraska, and his Ph.D. summa cum laude from the University of Chicago. Professor Sears is the author of several books and scores of popular and technical papers. Among his books are: *Deserts on the March, This Is Our World, Life and Environment,* and *Charles Darwin.*

WILLIAM E. SIRI, biophysicist at the University of California in Berkeley, is president of the Sierra Club and a long time leader and participant in mountaineering expeditions. He was leader of the Peruvian Expedition in 1952, the California Himalayan Expedition in 1954, a Bolivian Expedition in 1957, an Antarctic expedition in 1957–1958, and was deputy leader and scientific director of the American Mount Everest Expedition in 1963. His research specialty includes high altitude physiology.

CHARLES H. STODDARD was appointed director of the Bureau of Land Management, Department of the Interior, in 1963. He is a graduate forester, an owner of a tree farm in Northern Wisconsin, and has been a private consultant in resource conservation in the Lake states. Prior to this, he was director of the Resources Program Staff in the Office of the Secretary of the Interior and earlier served as research associate with Resources for the Future. Mr. Stoddard now serves as secretarial representative for the President's Quetico-Superior Committee.

EDGAR WAYBURN, M.D., is the immediate past president of the Sierra Club and currently vice-president. He is former president of Trustees for Conservation and the Federation of Western Outdoor Clubs and was chairman of the Eighth Biennial Wilderness Conference. A San Francisco internist and president of the San Francisco Medical Society in 1965, he is an associate clinical professor of medicine at Stanford University and the University of California. He was chairman of the Sierra Club's conservation committee for many years, is a director of the club, and a regular contributor to its *Bulletin.* Western wilderness is his special concern, and he has traveled in it and studied it extensively.

PEGGY WAYBURN, Chairman of the Ninth Biennial Wilderness Conference Committee, is a free-lance writer and a frequent contributor to the *Sierra Club Bulletin*. An active mountaineer and conservationist, as well as a mother of four, she served as Secretary for the Seventh and Eighth Wilderness Conferences. She is a member and director of many community organizations including the Citizen's Committee for Regional Recreation and Parks and the Point Reyes Foundation.

ACKNOWLEDGMENTS

Producing a Wilderness Conference is roughly analagous to producing a play. First must come the idea—the theme to be developed. Then comes the exploration of how best to put it over. An outstanding cast of speakers must be assembled and the timing of the performance perfected. For all of this, the Conference Committee of the Wilderness Conference is responsible; and no Broadway producer could ask for a more gifted or dedicated group than the planners of the Ninth Conference.

The conference speakers, of course, must write their own lines. This year's speakers were outstanding for their wit and wisdom as well as for a highly distinguished performance.

But even with the excellent planners and performers, the Wilderness Conference could not succeed without the many people who labor long and hard behind the scenes. The program lists such items as *registration, exhibits, art work, finance, publicity,* etc. Spelled out, this means literally hundreds of hours of devoted effort: it means the work of dozens of people with talent, endurance, and enthusiasm. The Sierra Club members, who (under the superb leadership of Genny Schumacher) handled the demanding jobs and the myriad details, achieved what many professionals do not: a top-notch performance that went off without a hitch.

Finally, the Wilderness Conference has to be paid for. The Ninth Conference was most fortunate to have many angels—hundreds of interested people as well as several members of the business community—all of whom gave what they could to help insure its success.

The Wilderness Conference is acclaimed for its many unique aspects. Surely none is more noteworthy than the fact that its production is achieved by volunteers, who take their only reward in the satisfaction of a job well done. The Sierra Club, the conference attendants, the community, and the readers of this book are deeply indebted to them all.

P.W.

THE NINTH BIENNIAL WILDERNESS CONFERENCE

CONFERENCE COMMITTEE

Peggy Wayburn, *chairman;* Genny Schumacher, *assistant;* Randal F. Dickey, Jr., James P. Gilligan, Robert V. Golden, Chauncey D. Leake, T. Eric Reynolds, William E. Siri, Edgar Wayburn

ARRANGEMENTS

Kenneth and Dona Gooden, *registration;* Lelia Crouch, *exhibits;* Roberta Ferguson, Bill Losh, Elizabeth Wilson, *publicity;* Ollo Baldauf, Robert Cranmer, William Fuller, Dan Gridley, Shi Pratini, *decorations and art work;* Dinny McAllister, *hostesses;* Ted Grubb, *field trip;* Doris Leonard, *transcription;* Stanley R. Dickover, Jr., *timekeeper;* Alice Donovan, *information desk;* Janet Sherwin, *special assignments;* Fred H. Smith, IV, *finance.*

COOPERATING ORGANIZATIONS

United States Forest Service
National Park Service
Junior League of San Francisco, Inc.
Belvedere Scientific Fund
Lurline B. Roth Charity Foundation
Foundation for Environmental Design
Sierra Club Foundation
Pacific Gas and Electric Company
Pacific Telephone and Telegraph Company
Richfield Oil Company
Standard Oil Company of California

SAN FRANCISCO HILTON · SAN FRANCISCO · APRIL 2-3, 1965

Sponsored by the Sierra Club